CYBERSPACE OPERATIONS AND ELECTROMAGNETIC WARFARE

AUGUST 2021

HEADQUARTERS DEPARTMENT OF THE ARMY

Other books we publish on Amazon.com

RUSSIA "NEW LOOK" COMBINED ARMS COMBAT MANUAL
PLATOON, SQUAD, TANK

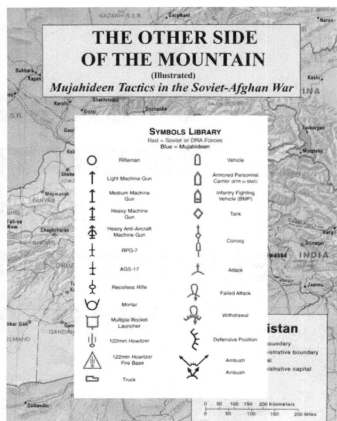

THE OTHER SIDE OF THE MOUNTAIN
(Illustrated)
Mujahideen Tactics in the Soviet-Afghan War

The Bear Went Over the Mountain
Soviet Combat Tactics In Afghanistan

RUSSIA "NEW LOOK" COMBAT TACTICS

Coming Soon

Foreword

Over the past two decades of persistent conflict, the Army has deployed its most capable communications systems ever. During this time, U.S. forces have continued to dominate cyberspace and the electromagnetic spectrum while conducting counterinsurgency operations in Afghanistan and Iraq against enemies and adversaries who lack the ability to challenge our technological superiority. However, in recent years, regional peers have demonstrated formidable capabilities in hybrid operational environments. These capabilities threaten the Army's dominance in both cyberspace and the electromagnetic spectrum.

The Department of Defense information network-Army is an essential warfighting platform that is a critical element of the command and control system and foundational to success in Army operations. Effectively operating, securing, and defending the network to maintain trust in its confidentiality, integrity, and availability is essential to commanders' success at all echelons. A commander who cannot access or trust communications and information systems or the data they carry risks the loss of lives, loss of critical resources, or mission failure. At the same time, our adversaries and enemies are also increasingly reliant on networks and networked weapons systems. The Army, as part of the joint force, must be prepared to exploit or deny our adversaries and enemies the operational advantages that these networks and systems provide.

As the Army shifts its focus to large-scale combat operations against regional peers, we must anticipate that these threat actors will persistently attempt to infiltrate, exploit, and degrade access to our networks and data. In the future, as adversary and enemy capabilities grow, our continued dominance of cyberspace and the electromagnetic spectrum will become less certain, while at the same time our ability to access cyberspace and spectrum-dependent capabilities will become both more challenging and more critical to fight and win in multiple domains.

Leveraging cyberspace and electromagnetic warfare effects throughout the competition continuum is key to achieving relative advantages through cyberspace and the electromagnetic spectrum while denying the same to our enemies and adversaries. To achieve these positions of relative advantage, commanders must integrate and synchronize cyberspace operations and electromagnetic warfare with all other available military capabilities using a combined arms approach. Moreover, intelligence, signal, information advantage activities, space, and fires capabilities are all critical to successful planning, synchronization, and execution of cyberspace operations and electromagnetic warfare. Commanders and staffs integrate and synchronize all of these capabilities across multiple domains and warfighting functions to maximize complementary effects in and through cyberspace and the electromagnetic spectrum.

FM 3-12 defines and describes the principles and tactics to address challenges in the operational environment while providing an overview of cyberspace operations, electromagnetic warfare, and their planning, integration, and synchronization through the operations process. It describes the units that conduct these operations and how they enable accomplishment of commanders' objectives in Army operations.

Due to the rapid evolution of friendly and threat capabilities, tactics, techniques, and procedures in cyberspace and the electromagnetic spectrum, the Cyber Center of Excellence will review and update FM 3-12 and supporting publications frequently in order to keep pace with the continuously evolving operational environment.

NEIL S. HERSEY
Major General, U.S. Army
Commanding

Other books we publish on Amazon.com

Russia Land-Based Electronic Warfare/RUMINT

R-330Zh Zhitel
R-934BMV
1L267 Moskva-1
Leer-2 Tigr-M REI PP
1L262E SPR-2M Rtut-BM
1RL257E Krasukha-S4
R-378B Borisoglebsk-2B

Customer reviews
⭐⭐⭐⭐☆ 4 out of 5

CHINA ELECTRONIC WARFARE WEAPONS/RUMINT

Customer reviews
⭐⭐⭐⭐☆ 4 out of 5

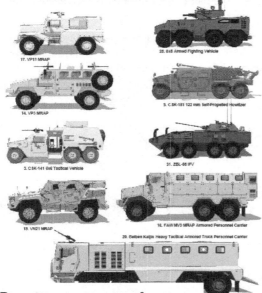

CHINA MRAPs, ARMORED CARS, ARMORED PERSONNEL CARRIERS & ARMORED ASSAULT VEHICLES

17. VP11 MRAP
28. 8x8 Armed Fighting Vehicle
14. VP5 MRAP
3. C SK-181 122 mm Self-Propelled Howitzer
3. C SK-141 6x6 Tactical Vehicle
31. ZBL-08 IFV
18. VN21 MRAP
16. FAW MV3 MRAP Armored Personnel Carrier
29. Beiben Kaijia Heavy Tactical Armored Truck Personnel Carrier

Customer reviews
⭐⭐⭐⭐⭐ 5 out of 5

RUSSIA MRAPs, ARMORED CARS, ARMORED PERSONNEL CARRIERS & ARMORED ASSAULT VEHICLES

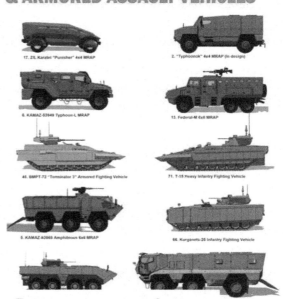

17. ZIL Karatel "Punisher" 4x4 MRAP
2. "Typhoonok" 4x4 MRAP (in design)
6. KAMAZ-53949 Typhoon-L MRAP
13. Federal-M 6x6 MRAP
45. BMPT-72 "Terminator 3" Armored Fighting Vehicle
71. T-15 Heavy Infantry Fighting Vehicle
5. KAMAZ-43969 Amphibious 6x6 MRAP
66. Kurganets-25 Infantry Fighting Vehicle
"K" MRAP

Customer reviews
⭐⭐⭐⭐⭐ 5 out of 5

Field Manual
No. 3-12

Headquarters
Department of the Army
Washington, D.C., 24 August 2021

Cyberspace Operations and Electromagnetic Warfare

Contents

Page

PREFACE v

INTRODUCTION vii

Chapter 1   **OPERATIONAL ENVIRONMENT OVERVIEW** 1-1
Overview of the Operational Environment 1-1
Cyberspace and the Electromagnetic Spectrum 1-1

Section I – Core Competencies and Fundamental Principles 1-3
Core Competencies 1-3
Fundamental Principles 1-4

Section II – Operational Environment 1-4
Cyberspace Domain 1-5
Electromagnetic Spectrum 1-7
Trends and Characteristics 1-8
Conflict and Competition 1-11

Section III – Contributions to the Warfighting Functions 1-12
Command and Control 1-12
Movement and Maneuver 1-13
Intelligence 1-14
Fires 1-15
Sustainment 1-15
Protection 1-15

Chapter 2   **CYBERSPACE OPERATIONS AND ELECTROMAGNETIC WARFARE FUNDAMENTALS** 2-1

Section I – Cyberspace Operations 2-1
Joint Force and Army 2-3
Department of Defense Information Network Operations 2-4
Defensive Cyberspace Operations 2-4
Offensive Cyberspace Operations 2-5
Cyberspace Actions 2-5

Section II – Electromagnetic Warfare 2-8
Electromagnetic Attack 2-8
Electromagnetic Protection 2-11
Electromagnetic Support 2-14

DISTRIBUTION RESTRICTION: Approved for public release; distribution is unlimited.

*This publication supersedes FM 3-12, dated 11 April 2017.

Electromagnetic Warfare Reprogramming... 2-15

Section III – Interrelationship with other Operations 2-16
Intelligence Operations 2-16
Space Operations 2-16
Information Operations 2-18

Chapter 3   ARMY ORGANIZATIONS AND COMMAND AND CONTROL 3-1

Section I – Army Cyberspace Operations Organizational Structure 3-1
United States Army Cyber Command... 3-1
Army Information Warfare Operations Center 3-2

Section II – Electromagnetic Warfare Organizations 3-3
Electromagnetic Warfare Platoon (Brigade Combat Team) 3-3
Intelligence, Information, Cyber, Electromagnetic Warfare, and Space
    Detachment 3-4

Section III – Cyberspace Electromagnetic Activities at Corps and Below........ 3-4
Commander's Role 3-4
Cyberspace Electromagnetic Activities Section.. 3-5
Cyberspace Electromagnetic Activities Working Group 3-8
Staff and Support at Corps and Below.. 3-8

Chapter 4   INTEGRATION THROUGH THE OPERATIONS PROCESS 4-1

Section I – The Operations Process... 4-1
Planning 4-2
Preparation.. 4-3
Execution 4-3
Assessment.. 4-4

Section II –Integrating Processes 4-4
Intelligence Preparation of the Battlefield 4-5
Information Collection 4-8
Targeting 4-11
Risk Management 4-18
Knowledge Management 4-20

Appendix A   ARMY METHODOLOGIES USED FOR PLANNING ACTIVITIES A-1

Appendix B   RULES OF ENGAGEMENT AND UNITED STATES CODE B-1

Appendix C   INTEGRATION WITH UNIFIED ACTION PARTNERS......................................C-1

**Appendix D   NATIONAL, DEPARTMENT OF DEFENSE, ARMY RESERVE AND JOINT
CYBERSPACE AND ELECTROMAGNETIC WARFARE ORGANIZATIONS........D-1**

Appendix E   REQUEST FOR SUPPORT...E-1

Appendix F   ELECTROMAGNETIC WARFARE REPROGRAMMING....................................F-1

Appendix G   TRAINING..G-1

GLOSSARY Glossary-1

REFERENCES... References-1

INDEX Index-1

Figures

Figure 1-1. Cyberspace operations and electromagnetic warfare logic chart 1-2
Figure 1-2. Relationship between the cyberspace network layers 1-6

Figure 1-3. The electromagnetic spectrum 1-8

Figure 1-4. Congestion in cyberspace and the electromagnetic spectrum 1-9

Figure 1-5. Cyberspace and the electromagnetic spectrum in a contested environment............1-10

Figure 2-1. Cyberspace operations taxonomy 2-3

Figure 2-2. Cyberspace operations missions and actions 2-6

Figure 2-3. Electromagnetic warfare taxonomy 2-8

Figure 4-1. The operations process and integrating processes..4-5

Figure A-1. Annex C, Appendix 12...A-16

Figure D-1. Cyber mission force team allocations D-6

Figure D-2. National electromagnetic spectrum operations organizational structure. D-9

Figure E-1. Routing process when requesting offensive cyberspace operations support.............E-3

Figure E-2. Routing process when requesting defensive cyberspace operations-internal defensive
measures support E-5

Figure E-3. Routing process for defensive cyberspace operations-internal defensive measures
(non-Department of Defense information network) and defensive cyberspace
operations-response actions support..E-6

Figure E-4. Joint tactical airstrike request form..E-11

Figure E-5. Electromagnetic attack request. E-13

Tables

Table 4-1. Targeting crosswalk 4-13

Table A-1. Step 1: Receipt of mission A-3

Table A-2. Step 2: Mission analysis A-6

Table A-3. Step 3: Course of action development A-9

Table A-4. Step 4: Course of action analysis and war-gaming A-11

Table A-5. Step 5: Course of action comparison A-12

Table A-6. Step 6: Course of action approval A-13

Table A-7. Step 7: Orders production, dissemination, and transition..A-14

Table B-1. United States Code with specific cyberspace roles...B-4

Table B-2. Federal cyberspace security laws and policies protecting United States citizens B-5

Table D-1. Elements of the cyber mission force and their associated teams D-5

Table E-1. Airborne cyberspace attack, electromagnetic attack, or electromagnetic support
request tool E-10

Other books we publish on Amazon.com

China Surface-to-Air Missile Systems

Customer reviews
★★★★⯨ 4.5 out of 5

Russia Surface-to-Air Missile Systems

Customer reviews
★★★★☆ 4 out of 5

CHINA UAV, UCAV, SUICIDE DRONES & SPACEPLANES

Customer reviews
★★★★★ 5 out of 5

Armata Universal Combat Platform

Customer reviews
★★⯨☆☆ 3.5 out of 5

Preface

FM 3-12 provides tactics and procedures for coordinating, integrating, and synchronizing Army cyberspace operations and electromagnetic warfare to support unified land operations and joint operations. FM 3-12 explains Army cyberspace operations and electromagnetic warfare fundamentals, terms, and definitions. This publication describes how commanders and staffs can integrate cyberspace operations and electromagnetic warfare into unified land operations. This publication provides overarching guidance to commanders and staffs on Army cyberspace operations and electromagnetic warfare at all echelons. This publication supersedes FM 3-12, dated 11 April 2017.

The principal audience for FM 3-12 is all members of the profession of arms. Commanders and staffs of Army headquarters serving as a joint task force or multinational headquarters should also apply joint or multinational doctrine concerning the range of military operations and joint or multinational forces. Trainers and educators throughout the Army will also use this publication.

Commanders, staffs, and subordinates ensure their decisions and actions comply with applicable United States, international, and in some cases, host-nation laws and regulations. Commanders at all levels ensure their Soldiers operate according to the law of war and the rules of engagement (See FM 6-27). They also adhere to the Army Ethic as described in ADP 1.

FM 3-12 uses joint terms where applicable. Selected joint and Army terms and definitions appear in both the glossary and the text. This publication is not the proponent for any Army terms. Terms and definitions for which FM 3-12 is the source publication are boldfaced in the text. For other definitions shown in the text, the term is italicized and the number of the proponent publication follows the definition.

FM 3-12 applies to the Active Army, Army National Guard or Army National Guard of the United States, and United States Army Reserve, unless otherwise stated.

The proponent of FM 3-12 is the United States Army Cyber Center of Excellence. The preparing agency is the Doctrine Division, United States Army Cyber Center of Excellence. Send comments and recommendations on a DA Form 2028 (*Recommended Changes to Publications and Blank Forms*) to Commander, United States. Army Cyber Center of Excellence and Fort Gordon, ATTN: ATZH-OP-D (FM 3-12), 506 Chamberlain Avenue, Fort Gordon, GA, 30905-5735; by e-mail to usarmy.gordon.cyber-coe.mbx.gord-fg-doctrine@mail.mil.

Other titles we publish on Amazon.com:

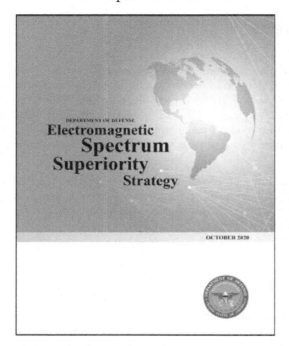

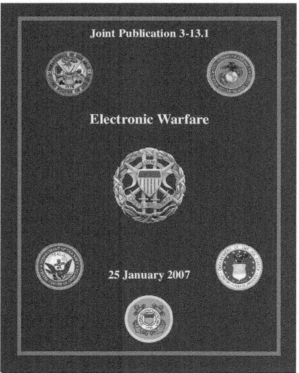

Introduction

FM 3-12 provides Army doctrine on using cyberspace electromagnetic activities to integrate and synchronize cyberspace operations and electromagnetic warfare into operations while managing assigned portions of the electromagnetic spectrum in support of unified land operations. FM 3-12 defines and provides an understanding of Army cyberspace operations, electromagnetic warfare, statutory and title authorities, roles, relationships, responsibilities, and capabilities to support Army and joint operations. It expands upon the methods by which Army forces conduct offensive and defensive cyberspace operations and addresses how commanders and staff integrate tailored cyberspace and electromagnetic warfare capabilities across the range of military operations.

FM 3-12 nests with and supports joint cyberspace operations and electromagnetic warfare doctrine and ADP 3-0, Operations, and provides the doctrinal context to address the relationship among the Army's operations process and cyberspace operations and electromagnetic warfare. To understand the fundamentals of integrating and synchronizing cyberspace operations and electromagnetic warfare, readers should be familiar with ADP 2-0, ADP 3-0, ADP 3-19, ADP 3-37, ADP 3-90, ADP 5-0, ADP 6-0, FM 3-09, FM 3-13, FM 3-55, FM 6-0, ATP 2-01.3, JP 3-12, and JP 3-85.

FM 3-12 describes how personnel conducting cyberspace electromagnetic activities integrate and synchronize cyberspace operations and electromagnetic warfare functions and capabilities across warfighting functions, defend the network, and provide commanders critical capabilities at all levels during unified land operations.

FM 3-12 contains four chapters and seven appendixes:

Chapter 1 outlines how cyberspace operations and electromagnetic warfare support the Army forces during the conduct of unified land operations. It provides an overview of the aspects of an operational environment in which units perform cyberspace operations and electromagnetic warfare. This chapter also details how cyberspace operations and electromagnetic warfare support the Army warfighting functions.

Chapter 2 details the types of cyberspace operations and electromagnetic warfare and their associated tasks and common effects. It also discusses the interrelationship between cyberspace operations and electromagnetic warfare with other types of Army operations.

Chapter 3 provides an overview of the joint and Army organizations that conduct cyberspace operations and electromagnetic warfare. It also describes the cyberspace electromagnetic activities section roles and responsibilities at echelon. This chapter discusses the interactions between the cyberspace electromagnetic activities section and other staff sections and explains the role of the cyberspace electromagnetic activities working group.

Chapter 4 describes how commanders and staffs integrate and synchronize cyberspace operations and electromagnetic warfare through the operations process. This chapter further details key inputs and outputs related to intelligence preparation of the battlefield, information collection, targeting, risk management, and knowledge management.

Appendix A describes the two most common Army decision-making methodologies (the Army design methodology and the military decision-making process) and procedures for these methodologies to plan, integrate, and synchronize cyberspace operations and electromagnetic warfare with the operations process and integrating processes.

Appendix B describes the rules of engagement and applicable sections of the United States Code associated with cyberspace operations and electromagnetic warfare. It includes a table with all cyberspace operations and electromagnetic warfare related to the United States Code (title authorities). Appendix B also consists of a table with a list of federal laws protecting United States civilians' information and privacy rights.

Appendix C discusses considerations when conducting cyberspace operations and electromagnetic warfare as part of a joint force or with unified action partners.

Appendix D discusses the national, Department of Defense, and Army Reserve components that support cyberspace operations. This appendix also provides an overview of the United States Cyber Command and its subordinate joint organizations that deliver cyberspace operations and electromagnetic warfare support to Army commanders using cyberspace mission forces.

Appendix E discusses how Army units request cyberspace operations and electromagnetic warfare support when operating in a joint environment. Graphic depictions display the request for support processes for both offensive and defensive cyberspace operations.

Appendix F provides general procedures for conducting electromagnetic warfare reprogramming. It describes the four phases of electromagnetic warfare reprogramming and its three major categories and actions.

Appendix G provides an overview of Soldier training and expands on training for those seeking a career in cyberspace and electromagnetic warfare.

Chapter 1

Operational Environment Overview

This chapter describes the aspects of the operational environment in which the Army conducts cyberspace operations and electromagnetic warfare. It describes cyberspace and electromagnetic warfare forces' core competencies and lays out the fundamental principles of cyberspace operations and electromagnetic warfare. This chapter discusses interrelationships and interdependencies between cyberspace operations, electromagnetic warfare, and the warfighting functions.

OVERVIEW OF THE OPERATIONAL ENVIRONMENT

1-1. Cyberspace operations and electromagnetic warfare (EW) play an essential role in the Army's conduct of unified land operations as part of a joint force and in coordination with unified action partners. *Cyberspace operations* are the employment of cyberspace capabilities where the primary purpose is to achieve objectives in or through cyberspace (JP 3-0). *Electromagnetic warfare* is a military action involving the use of electromagnetic and directed energy to control the electromagnetic spectrum or to attack the enemy (JP 3-85).

1-2. Cyberspace is one of the five domains of warfare and uses a portion of the electromagnetic spectrum (EMS) for operations, for example, Bluetooth, Wi-Fi, and satellite transport. Therefore, cyberspace operations and EW require frequency assignment, management, and coordination performed by spectrum management operations. Spectrum management operations consist of four key functions—spectrum management, frequency assignment, host-nation coordination, and policy adherence. Spectrum management operations include preventing and mitigating frequency conflicts and electromagnetic interference (EMI) between friendly forces and host nations during Army operations (refer to ATP 6-02.70).

CYBERSPACE AND THE ELECTROMAGNETIC SPECTRUM

1-3. Cyberspace and the EMS are critical for success in today's operational environment (OE). U.S. and adversary forces alike rely heavily on cyberspace and EMS-dependent technologies for command and control, information collection, situational understanding, and targeting. Achieving relative superiority in cyberspace and the EMS gives commanders an advantage over adversaries and enemies. By conducting cyberspace operations and EW, commanders can limit adversaries' available courses of action, diminish their ability to gain momentum, degrade their command and control, and degrade their ability to operate effectively in the other domains.

1-4. Commanders must leverage cyberspace and EW capabilities using a combined arms approach to seize, retain, and exploit the operational initiative. Effective use of cyberspace operations and EW require commanders and staffs to conduct cyberspace electromagnetic activities (CEMA). *Cyberspace electromagnetic activities* is the process of planning, integrating, and synchronizing cyberspace operations and electromagnetic warfare in support of unified land operations (ADP 3-0). By integrating and synchronizing cyberspace operations and EW, friendly forces gain an information advantage across multiple domains and lines of operations. Figure 1-1 on page 1-2 illustrates how cyberspace operations and EW contribute to Army operations.

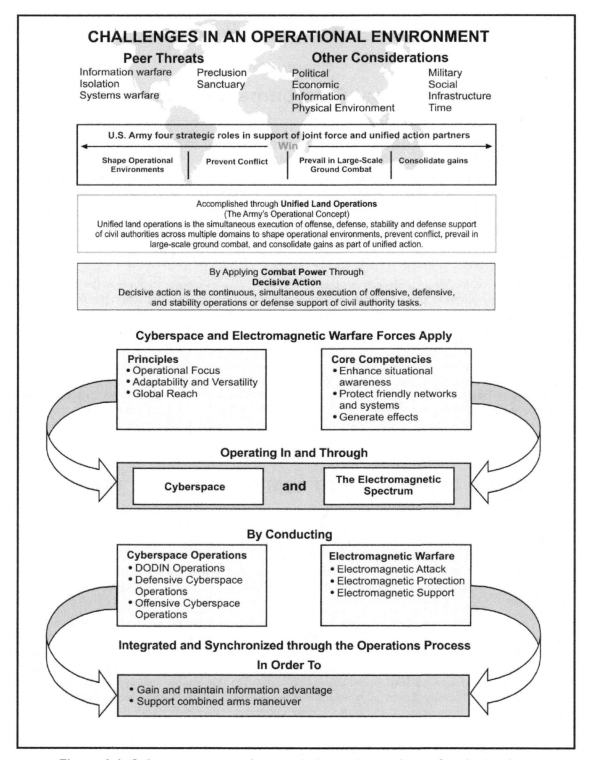

Figure 1-1. Cyberspace operations and electromagnetic warfare logic chart

SECTION I – CORE COMPETENCIES AND FUNDAMENTAL PRINCIPLES

1-5.   The Army's reliance on networked systems and weapons necessitates highly trained forces to protect warfighting systems and networks dependent upon access to cyberspace and the EMS. Cyberspace and the EMS are heavily congested due to the high volume of friendly, neutral, and adversary use, and contested due to adversary actions.

1-6.   Adversaries continue to develop sophisticated weapons and networked systems that project power through or depend on cyberspace and the EMS. The Army employs cyberspace and EW capabilities as part of a joint and combined arms approach to defeat threat activities in cyberspace and the EMS, protect friendly forces, and enable friendly freedom of action across the conflict continuum. Army cyberspace and EW forces apply the following core competencies and underlying fundamental principles to ensure friendly forces gain and maintain positions of relative advantage.

CORE COMPETENCIES

1-7.   Cyberspace forces and EW professionals are organized, trained, and equipped to provide the following core competencies that deliver essential and enduring capabilities to the Army—
- Enable situational understanding.
- Protect friendly personnel and capabilities.
- Deliver effects.

CREATE UNDERSTANDING

1-8.   Cyberspace forces execute cyberspace intelligence, surveillance, and reconnaissance in and through the information environment to identify and understand adversary networks, systems, and processes. This information enables commanders to understand adversary capabilities and vulnerabilities, thereby enhancing the commanders' ability to prioritize and deliver effects.

1-9.   EW professionals surveil the EMS to collect combat information used to characterize adversary use of the EMS and understand the integration of adversary emitter systems arrays at echelon. This information enables understanding friendly vulnerabilities and threat capabilities while allowing commanders to prioritize and deliver effects.

PROTECT FRIENDLY PERSONNEL AND CAPABILITIES

1-10.   Cyberspace forces defend networks, warfighting platforms, capabilities, and data from ongoing or imminent malicious cyberspace activity. By protecting critical networks and systems, cyberspace forces help maintain the Army's ability to conduct operations and project power across all domains.

1-11.   EW forces, in coordination with the G-6 or S-6 and in support of the commander's directive, implement and enhance measures to protect friendly personnel, facilities, warfighting platforms, capabilities, and equipment from adverse effects in the EMS. EW forces recommend measures to mask or control friendly emissions from enemy detection and deny adversaries the ability to locate and target friendly formations. EW forces detect and mitigate enemy attacks in or through the EMS to maintain the Army's ability to conduct operations and project power across all domains.

DELIVER EFFECTS

1-12.   Cyberspace forces deliver cyberspace effects against adversary networks, systems, and weapons. These effects enhance the Army's ability to conduct operations, reduce adversary combat power, and project power across all domains.

1-13.   EW professionals deliver effects in the EMS against adversary networks, systems, and weapons. These actions reduce adversary combat power, protect friendly forces, and enhance friendly forces and weapons' lethality.

FUNDAMENTAL PRINCIPLES

1-14. Fundamental principles are basic rules or assumptions of central importance that guide how cyberspace and EW professionals' approach and conduct cyberspace operations and EW. These fundamental principles are—

- Operational focus.
- Adaptability and versatility.
- Global reach.

OPERATIONAL FOCUS

1-15. Cyberspace and EW forces execute missions in support of a commander's overarching operational design. When properly integrated and synchronized as part of a combined arms approach, cyberspace and EW capabilities can produce layered dilemmas for the adversary in multiple domains and enhance relative combat power. To accomplish this, cyberspace and EW staff must collaborate across all warfighting functions.

ADAPTABILITY AND VERSATILITY

1-16. Cyberspace and EW forces conduct operations using capabilities that are adaptable to a variety of mission requirements. Cyberspace and EW capabilities vary in both the size of the force employed and the magnitude or scope of effects created. Depending on mission requirements, cyberspace and EW capabilities may be used as primary or supporting efforts for decisive, shaping or sustaining operations.

GLOBAL REACH

1-17. The nature of the cyberspace domain increases the operational reach of cyberspace and EW forces. Combat mission force(s) and EW professionals deliver strategic, operational, or tactical effects worldwide from remote, co-located, or forward operating positions.

SECTION II – OPERATIONAL ENVIRONMENT

1-18. An *operational environment* is a composite of the conditions, circumstances, and influences that affect the employment of capabilities and bear on the decisions of the commander (JP 3-0). Conditions in cyberspace and the EMS often change rapidly and can positively or negatively impact a commander's ability to achieve mission objectives. Friendly, neutral, adversary, and enemy actions in cyberspace and the EMS can create near-instantaneous effects on the battlefield or in garrison. Given the global nature of cyberspace and the EMS, these actions can impact a commander's OE even though the actions may originate or terminate beyond that OE. Cyberspace and EW effects also cross through and impact multiple domains simultaneously. For these reasons, commanders must gain and maintain an in-depth understanding of the OE that extends beyond the land domain to the multi-domain extended battlefield to seize, exploit, and retain operational initiative.

1-19. *Operational initiative* is the setting of tempo and terms of action throughout an operation (ADP 3-0). By gaining and maintaining positions of relative advantage, including information advantage in and through cyberspace and the EMS, commanders can seize and retain the operational initiative. To gain and maintain information advantage, commanders must account for the temporal nature of information and the temporary nature of many cyberspace and EW effects. On average, the relative operational advantage that a commander can gain from a piece of information or from a cyberspace or EW effect degrades over time. This means that a commander who takes action first, on average, will obtain a greater information advantage from a similar piece of information or effect than a commander who acts later. In this way, the commander who can sense, understand, decide, act, and assess faster than an opponent will generally obtain the greatest information advantage.

1-20. Commanders can use cyberspace and EW capabilities to gain enhanced situational awareness and understanding of the enemy through reconnaissance and sensing activities. These reconnaissance and sensing activities can augment and enhance the understanding a commander gains from information collection and intelligence processes. Commanders can also use cyberspace and EW capabilities to decide and act faster than an adversary or enemy. By protecting friendly information systems and signals from disruption or exploitation by an adversary or enemy, a commander can ensure command and control and maintain tactical and operational surprise. Conversely, a commander might use cyberspace and EW capabilities to slow or degrade an enemy's decision-making processes by disrupting enemy sensors, communications, or data processing. To make effective use of cyberspace and EW capabilities to achieve an information advantage, a commander must plan early to integrate cyberspace operations and EW actions fully into the overall scheme of maneuver.

CYBERSPACE DOMAIN

1-21. *Cyberspace* is a global domain within the information environment consisting of the interdependent networks of information technology infrastructures and resident data, including the Internet, telecommunications networks, computer systems, and embedded processors and controllers (JP 3-12). Cyberspace operations require the use of links and nodes located in other physical domains to perform logical functions that create effects in cyberspace that then permeate throughout the physical domains using both wired networks and the EMS.

1-22. The use of cyberspace is essential to operations. The Army conducts cyberspace operations and supporting activities as part of both Army and joint operations. Because cyberspace is a global communications and data-sharing medium, it is inherently joint, inter-organizational, multinational, and often a shared resource, with signal and intelligence maintaining significant equities. Friendly, enemy, adversary, and host-nation networks, communications systems, computers, cellular phone systems, social media websites, and technical infrastructures are all part of cyberspace.

1-23. To aid the planning and execution of cyberspace operations, cyberspace is sometimes visualized in three layers. These layers are interdependent, but each layer has unique attributes that affect operations. Cyberspace operations generally traverse all three layers of cyberspace but may target effects at one or more specific layers. Planners must consider the challenges and opportunities presented by each layer of cyberspace as well as the interactions amongst the layers. Figure 1-2 on page 1-6 depicts the relationship between the three cyberspace layers. The three cyberspace layers are—
- The physical network layer.
- The logical network layer.
- The cyber-persona layer.

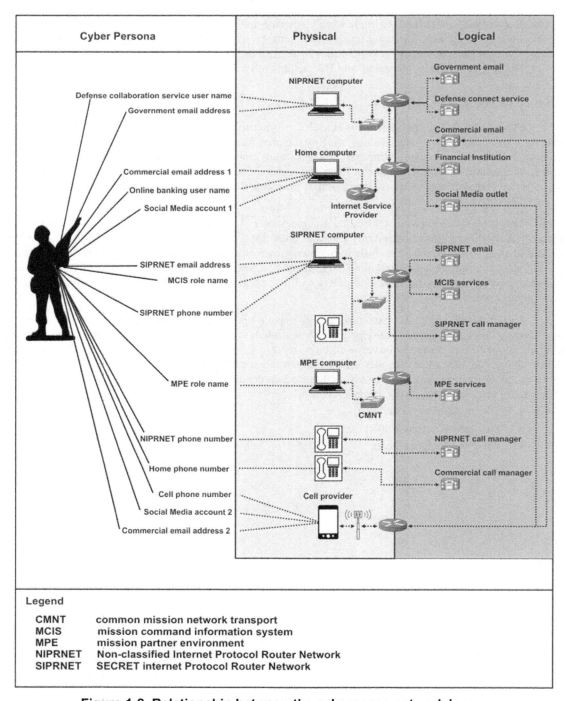

Figure 1-2. Relationship between the cyberspace network layers

PHYSICAL NETWORK LAYER

1-24.   The physical network layer consists of the information technology devices and infrastructure in the physical domains that provide storage, transport, and processing of information within cyberspace, to include data repositories and the connections that transfer data between network components (JP 3-12). Physical network components include the hardware and infrastructure such as computing devices, storage devices, network devices, and wired and wireless links. Components of the physical network layer require physical security measures to protect them from damage or unauthorized access, which, if left vulnerable, could allow a threat to gain access to both systems and critical data.

1-25.   Every physical component of cyberspace is owned by a public or private entity. The physical layer often crosses geo-political boundaries and is one of the reasons that cyberspace operations require multiple levels of joint and unified action partner coordination. Cyberspace planners use knowledge of the physical location of friendly, neutral, and adversary information technology systems and infrastructures to understand appropriate legal frameworks for cyberspace operations and to estimate impacts of those operations. Joint doctrine refers to portions of cyberspace, based on who owns or controls that space, as either blue, gray, or red cyberspace (refer to JP 3-12). This publication refers to these areas as friendly, neutral, or enemy cyberspace respectively.

LOGICAL NETWORK LAYER

1-26.   The logical network layer consists of those elements of the network related to one another in a way that is abstracted from the physical network, based on the logic programming (code) that drives network components (i.e., the relationships are not necessarily tied to a specific physical link or node, but to their ability to be addressed logically and exchange or process data) (JP 3-12). Nodes in the physical layer may logically relate to one another to form entities in cyberspace not tied to a specific node, path, or individual. Web sites hosted on servers in multiple physical locations where content can be accessed through a single uniform resource locator or web address provide an example. This may also include the logical programming to look for the best communications route, instead of the shortest physical route, to provide the information requested.

CYBER-PERSONA LAYER

1-27.   The cyber-persona layer is a view of cyberspace created by abstracting data from the logical network layer using the rules that apply in the logical network layer to develop descriptions of digital representations of an actor or entity identity in cyberspace, known as a cyber-persona (JP 3-12). Cyber-personas are not confined to a single physical or logical location and may link to multiple physical and logical network layers. When planning and executing cyberspace operations, staffs should understand that one actor or entity (user) may have multiple cyber-personas, using multiple identifiers in cyberspace. These various identifiers can include different work and personal emails and different identities on different Web forums, chatrooms, and social network sites.

1-28.   For example, an individual's account on a social media website, consisting of the username and digital information associated with that username, may be just one of that individual's cyber-personas. Conversely, multiple different users may share a single cyber-persona or set of cyber-personas. Planners must understand that enemy use of cyber-personas can make attributing responsibility for cyberspace actions difficult.

ELECTROMAGNETIC SPECTRUM

1-29.   The electromagnetic spectrum (EMS) - is a maneuver space essential for facilitating control within the operational environment (OE) and impacts all portions of the OE and military operations. Based on specific physical characteristics, the EMS is organized by frequency bands, including radio waves, microwaves, infrared radiation, visible light, ultraviolet radiation, x-rays, and gamma rays. Figure 1-3 on page 1-8 illustrates the range of standard frequencies in the EMS and some of the common devices operating in those frequencies.

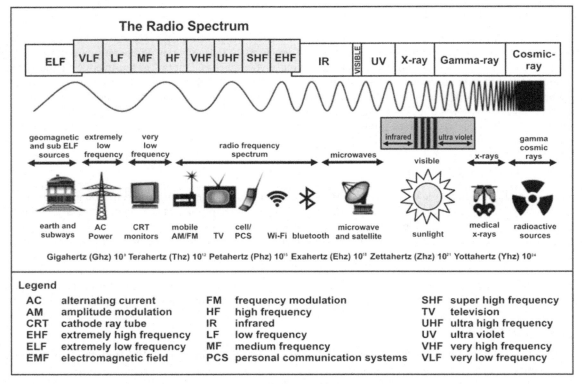

Figure 1-3. The electromagnetic spectrum

TRENDS AND CHARACTERISTICS

1-30.   The rapid proliferation of cyberspace and EMS capabilities has further congested an already challenging OE. In addition to competing with threat actors in cyberspace and the EMS, U.S. forces also encounter challenges resulting from neutral actors. Such neutral systems as commercial aircraft and airports, Worldwide Interoperability for Microwave Access, and commercial cellular infrastructures contribute to continuing congestion in cyberspace and the EMS. Figure 1-4 on page 1-9, depicts cyberspace and the EMS in a congested OE.

1-31.   Several key trends and characteristics impact a commander's ability to use cyberspace and the EMS. Such trends and characteristics include—

- Congested environments.
- Contested environments.
- Threats.
- Hazards.
- Terrain.

CONGESTED ENVIRONMENTS

1-32.   Both cyberspace and the EMS are increasingly congested environments that friendly, neutral, and threat actors use to transmit and process large amounts of information. Since 2000, the Army's use of networked information systems in almost every aspect of operations has increased tenfold. Neutral and threat actors have similarly expanded their use of cyberspace and the EMS for a wide range of military and non-military purposes.

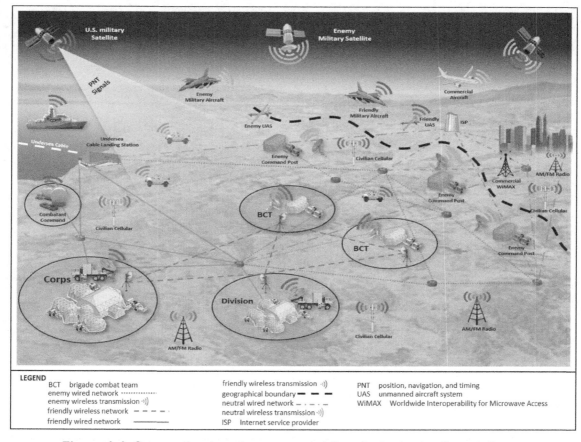

Figure 1-4. Congestion in cyberspace and the electromagnetic spectrum

CONTESTED ENVIRONMENTS

1-33.   As cyberspace and the EMS continue to become more congested, the capabilities of state and non-state actors to contest U.S. advantages in both areas have also expanded. State and non-state threats use a wide range of advanced technologies that may represent relatively inexpensive ways for a small or materially disadvantaged adversary to pose a significant threat to the United States. The application of low-cost cyberspace capabilities can provide an advantage against a technology-dependent nation or organization and an asymmetric advantage to those who could not otherwise effectively oppose U.S. military forces. Figure 1-5 on page 1-10, depicts an operational view of cyberspace and the EMS in a contested OE.

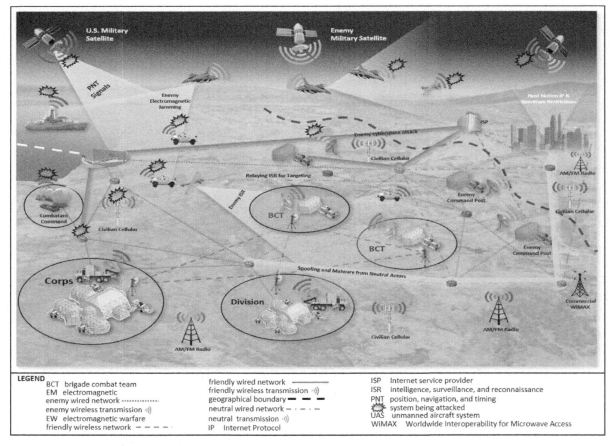

Figure 1-5. Cyberspace and the electromagnetic spectrum in a contested environment

THREATS

1-34. For every operation, threats are a fundamental part of an OE. A *threat* is any combination of actors, entities, or forces that have the capability and intent to harm United States forces, United States national interests, or the homeland (ADP 3-0). Threat is an umbrella term that includes any actor with the potential to harm the United States or its interests. Threats include—

- Enemies.
- Adversaries.
- Peer threats.
- Hybrid threats.
- Insider threats.

1-35. An *enemy* is a party identified as hostile against which the use of force is authorized (ADP 3-0). An enemy is also called a combatant and treated as such under the laws of war. Enemies will employ various advanced technologies to attack Army forces in cyberspace and EMS to disrupt or destroy the ability to conduct operations or collect information that will give friendly forces a strategic, operational, or tactical advantage.

1-36. An *adversary* is a party acknowledged as potentially hostile to a friendly party and against which the use of force may be envisaged (JP 3-0). Though an adversary is not treated as a combatant, the goal is still to prevent and deter conflict by keeping their activities within a desired state of cooperation and competition.

1-37. A peer threat is an adversary or enemy able to effectively oppose U.S. forces world-wide while enjoying a position of relative advantage in a specific region (ADP 3-0), including cyberspace and the EMS. Peer threats often have cyberspace and EW capabilities that are comparable to U.S. capabilities. Peer threats may employ these capabilities across the competition continuum to collect intelligence, delay the deployment of U.S. forces, degrade U.S. capabilities, and disrupt U.S. operations. Peer threats have electromagnetic attack (EA) capabilities such as telecommunications and EMS jamming equivalent to or better than U.S. forces. Peer threats can conduct advanced cyberspace attacks, including denial-of-service, various forms of phishing, eavesdropping, and malware.

1-38.   A *hybrid threat* is the diverse and dynamic combination of regular forces, irregular forces, or criminal elements unified to achieve mutually benefitting effects (ADP 3-0). Commanders and staffs must understand that the diversity of a hybrid threat complicates operations since hostility is coming from multiple actors operating from various geographical territories. A hybrid threat complicates the United States' efforts to identify, characterize, attribute, and respond to threats in cyberspace and the EMS.

1-39.   Organized crime or other non-state, illegitimate organizations often make sophisticated malware available for purchase or free, allowing even unsophisticated threat actors to acquire advanced capabilities at little to no cost. Because of the low barriers to entry and the potentially high payoff, the United States can expect an increasing number of adversaries to use cyberspace capabilities to attempt to negate U.S. advantages in military capability.

1-40.   An *insider threat* is a person with placement and access who intentionally causes loss or degradation of resources or capabilities or compromises the ability of an organization to accomplish its mission through espionage, providing support to international terrorism, or the unauthorized release or disclosure of information about the plans and intentions of United States military forces (AR 381-12). Insider threats may include spies within or working with U.S. forces, as well as personnel who may be unaware of their actions either through deception or third party manipulation. Insider threats present unique challenges because they are trusted individuals with authorized access to Army capabilities and sensitive operational information. Insider threats may include spies within or working with U.S. forces.

Note. Law enforcement and counterintelligence capabilities also operate in cyberspace during their efforts to neutralize criminal activities. Countering insider threats falls primarily within the purview of these organizations and outside the authorized activities of the cyberspace forces. However, information discovered in the course of authorized cyberspace operations may aid these other organizations.

HAZARDS

1-41.   A *hazard* is a condition with the potential to cause injury, illness, or death of personnel, damage to or loss of equipment or property, or mission degradation (JP 3-33). Disruption to cyberspace's physical infrastructure often occurs due to operator errors, industrial accidents, and natural disasters. These unpredictable events may have just as significant impact on operations as the actions of enemies. Recovery from accidents and hazardous incidents may require significant coordination external to the DOD or the temporary reliance on backup systems with which operators may be less familiar.

1-42.   Electromagnetic energy can also impact the operational capability of military forces, equipment, systems, and platforms. Various hazards from electromagnetic energy include electromagnetic environmental effects, electromagnetic compatibility issues, EMI, electromagnetic pulse, and electromagnetic radiation hazards.

1-43.   Electromagnetic radiation hazards include hazards of electromagnetic radiation to personnel; hazards of electromagnetic radiation to ordnance; hazards of electromagnetic radiation to fuels; and natural phenomena effects such as space weather, lightning, and precipitation static.

CONFLICT AND COMPETITION

1-44.   Army forces face continuous competition and conflict in cyberspace and the EMS from threats intending to diminish friendly capabilities. Commanders must seek and exploit opportunities for success in cyberspace and the EMS wherever and whenever authorized.

COMPETITION CONTINUUM

1-45.   Cyberspace operations, EW, and spectrum management operations take place across the competition continuum. The competition continuum describes a world of enduring competition conducted through a mixture of cooperation, competition below armed conflict, and armed conflict Superiority in cyberspace and the EMS enables U.S. forces to conduct operations to achieve the goals and accomplish the objectives assigned to them by the President and Secretary of Defense. Though U.S. forces may conduct cyberspace operations and EW during competition below the level of armed conflict, they are critical enablers to combat power when conducting large-scale combat operations during armed conflict. Competition below armed conflict consists of situations in which joint forces take actions outside of armed conflict against a strategic actor in pursuit of policy objectives.

1-46.   Spectrum management operations fulfill a crucial within the CEMA construct. Spectrum management operations take place across the entire competition continuum and ensure proper coordination of EMS activities spanning the entirety of military operations.

MULTI-DOMAIN EXTENDED BATTLEFIELD

1-47.   The enemy seeks to employ capabilities to create effects in multiple domains to counter U.S. interests and impede friendly operations. Threat actors will conduct activities in the information environment, space, and cyberspace to influence U.S. decision makers and disrupt the deployment of friendly forces. Land-based threats will attempt to impede joint force freedom of action across the air, land, maritime, space, and cyberspace domains. They will disrupt the EMS, sow confusion, and challenge the legitimacy of U.S. actions. Understanding how threats can present multiple dilemmas to Army forces in all domains helps Army commanders identify (or create), seize, and exploit their opportunities. Implementing operations security (OPSEC) is critical to protecting essential friendly information technology infrastructures, command and control, and targeting systems. *Operations security* is a capability that identifies and controls critical information, indicators of friendly force actions attendant to military operations and incorporates countermeasures to reduce the risk of an adversary exploiting vulnerabilities (JP 3-13.3).

POSITIONS OF RELATIVE ADVANTAGE IN CYBERSPACE AND THE ELECTROMAGNETIC SPECTRUM

1-48.   The Army conducts cyberspace operations and EW to attain positions of relative advantage in cyberspace and the EMS, to establish information superiority. A *position of relative advantage* is a location or the establishment of a favorable condition within the area of operations that provides the commander with temporary freedom of action to enhance combat power over an enemy or influence the enemy to accept risk and move to a position of disadvantage (ADP 3-0).

SECTION III – CONTRIBUTIONS TO THE WARFIGHTING FUNCTIONS

1-49.   This section describes how cyberspace operations and EW support the warfighting functions. It specifies the types of cyberspace operations and EW missions and actions that contribute to the various tasks related to each warfighting function.

COMMAND AND CONTROL

1-50.   Commanders rely heavily on cyberspace and the EMS for command and control. At corps and below, the network in the command-and-control system is the Department of Defense information network-Army (DODIN-A). The *Department of Defense information network-Army* is an Army-operated enclave of the DODIN that encompasses all Army information capabilities that collect, process, store, display, disseminate, and protect information worldwide (ATP 6-02.71). Signal forces establish, manage, secure, and defend the DODIN-A by conducting Department of Defense information network operations and maintaining cybersecurity compliance to prevent intrusions into the DODIN-A. For more information on DODIN operations, refer to FM 6-02 and ATP 6-02.71. The networks and systems that comprise the DODIN-A enable commanders to control units, have a shared understanding of the OE, and interact with subordinate units in near real-time.

1-51. EW supports command and control through electromagnetic protection (EP) to eliminate or mitigate the negative impact of friendly, neutral, enemy, or naturally occurring EMI on command-and-control systems. The frequency assignment and deconfliction tasks of spectrum management operations support EP (See ATP 6-02.70). Such EP tasks include—emission control, mitigating electromagnetic environmental effects, electromagnetic compatibility, electromagnetic masking, preemptive countermeasures, and electromagnetic warfare reprogramming. These tasks require integration with spectrum management operation for frequency management and deconfliction. Chapter 2 of this publication and ATP 3-12.3 details information on EP.

MOVEMENT AND MANEUVER

1-52. Cyberspace operations and EW enhance friendly forces commanders' movement and maneuver by disrupting adversary command and control, reducing adversary and increasing friendly situational awareness, and negatively affect the adversary's ability to make sound decisions. Due to the range and reach of cyberspace capabilities, cyberspace forces are often able to support friendly maneuver in close areas while simultaneously supporting deep area operations. For information on close and deep area operations, refer to FM 3-0. For techniques on deep operations, refer to ATP 3-94.2.

1-53. DODIN operations support movement and maneuver by establishing secure tactical networks that allow communications with friendly forces conducting operations laterally in close and deep areas, in addition to communications with higher headquarters in the rear area. Units use the DODIN-A as the primary means of communication during movement and maneuver. Satellite communications, combat net radios, and wired networks are elements of the DODIN-A used to synchronize operations, collaborate, understand the environment, and coordinate fires. The network enables near real-time updates to the common operational picture. The upper and lower tiers of the DODIN-A connect headquarters to subordinate, adjacent, and higher headquarters and unified action partners.

1-54. Offensive cyberspace operations (OCO) in coordination with other forms of fires also support movement and maneuver by opening avenues necessary to disperse and displace enemy forces. Synchronizing OCO with other fires sets conditions that enable maneuver to gain or exploit positions of relative advantage. OCO will be discussed in detail in Chapter 2.

1-55. EW assets support movement and maneuver by conducting operations to degrade, neutralize, or destroy enemy combat capabilities in the EMS. Defensive EA protects friendly forces from enemy attacks during movement and maneuver by denying the enemy the use of the EMS. Using friendly EA to counter radio-controlled devices, such as improvised explosive devices, drones, robots, or radio-guided munitions is an example of defensive EA. During defensive EA, EW assets conduct operations to degrade, neutralize, or destroy enemy combat capabilities in the EMS. EW assets conduct defensive EA by employing EA capabilities such as counter radio-controlled improvised explosive device electronic warfare and devices used for aircraft survivability. Offensive EA supports movement and maneuver by projecting power within the time and tempo of the scheme of maneuver. Electromagnetic jamming, electromagnetic intrusion, and electromagnetic probing are examples of offensive EA. Electromagnetic support (ES) supports movement and maneuver by providing combat information for a situational understanding of the OE.

1-56. A variety of EP tasks also support movement and maneuver. Spectrum managers and EW personnel deconflict friendly frequencies to prevent or mitigate frequency interference from friendly forces. Frequency deconfliction includes preventive and mitigating measures to ensure friendly radio devices used during movement and maneuver tasks do not cause frequency interference to the radios used by other friendly forces. Electromagnetic masking supports movement and maneuver by concealing electromagnetic signatures radiated by friendly forces' spectrum dependent systems during operations. Conducting emission control during movement and maneuver reduces electromagnetic signatures of friendly forces' spectrum dependent communications and navigational systems during movement and maneuver. EW forces also employ sensors before a movement as preemptive countermeasures. Electromagnetic security supports movement and maneuver by denying an enemy the ability to decipher information derived from electromagnetic energy that they intercept. These tasks are discussed in further detail in Chapter 2 of this publication and in ATP 3-12.3.

INTELLIGENCE

1-57.   Cyberspace operations, EW, and intelligence mutually identify the cyberspace and EMS aspects of the OE to provide recommendations for friendly courses of action during the military decision-making process. Cyberspace and EW forces support information collection that may be used by intelligence professionals. Conversely, intelligence operations provide products that enhance understanding of the OE, enable targeting, and support defense in cyberspace and the EMS. It is critical that information acquired through cyberspace operations and EW is standardized and reported to the intelligence community.

1-58.   Intelligence supports cyberspace operations through the intelligence process, intelligence preparation of the battlefield (IPB), and information collection. Intelligence at all echelons supports cyberspace operations and EW planning, and helps measure performance and effectiveness through battle damage assessment. Cyberspace planners leverage intelligence analysis, reporting, and production capabilities to understand the OE, develop plans and targets, and support operations throughout the operations process. In the context of cyberspace and the EMS, the OE includes network topology overlays that graphically depict how information flows and resides within the operational area and how the network transports data in and out of the area of interest.

INTELLIGENCE PREPARATION OF THE BATTLEFIELD

1-59.   During IPB, the staff considers how the adversary or enemy utilizes cyberspace and the EMS to achieve their objectives. Intelligence and CEMA staff also consider state and non-state actors with capability, access, and intent to affect friendly operations as they define and analyze the area of interest.

1-60.   Intelligence analysts, with support from other staff elements, evaluate enemy and adversary use of cyberspace and the EMS. This includes evaluating aspects such as—

- Adversary or enemy use of cyberspace and the EMS.
- Reliance on networked capabilities.
- Sophistication of cyberspace attack capabilities.
- Adversary cyberspace defense capabilities.
- Adversary EW capabilities.
- Network vulnerabilities (both adversary and friendly).
- Ability to synchronize cyberspace operations with other operations.
- Adversary use of social media for social engineering.

1-61.   When assessing the enemy or adversary courses of action, the intelligence staff considers how the enemy or adversary will include cyberspace and the EMS in its operations. The commander and staff should consider threat courses of action in cyberspace and the EMS when planning friendly operations. (See ATP 2-01.3 for more information about IPB).

1-62.   Weather (terrestrial and space) also affects operations in cyberspace and the EMS. In assessing weather effects, the staff considers key terrain in cyberspace and the EMS in relation to other aspects of the area of interest and the area of operations.

ELECTROMAGNETIC SUPPORT AND SIGNALS INTELLIGENCE

1-63.   ES and signals intelligence (SIGINT) are similar in function, but SIGINT requires separate authorities. EW personnel conduct ES to acquire information in support of a commander's maneuver plan. No requirement or restriction exists for EW personnel to have SIGINT authorities to conduct these activities.

1-64.   EW and SIGINT personnel both identify emitters in the EMS and may cue each other for targeting, but have distinct mission responsibilities. EW personnel characterize and identify emitters by analyzing external signals for immediate threat recognition and warning, force protection, and targeting. ES provides combat information that has a limited time value to support operations. ES information may be passed to intelligence units or staff for further SIGINT analysis depending on situation and authorities. SIGINT personnel analyze internal signal parameters to produce and disseminate intelligence, which requires SIGINT authorities.

FIRES

1-65.   OCO and EA tasks are part of the fires warfighting function. Cyberspace forces employ cyberspace attacks to deny, degrade, disrupt, and destroy or otherwise affect enemies' cyberspace or information-dependent capabilities. EW personnel employ EA to degrade, and neutralize the enemies' ability to use the EMS. Cyberspace and EW effects transcends beyond cyberspace and the EMS and may result in second-and-third-order effects that could impact the other physical domains.

1-66.   Army cyberspace and EW effects applied against enemy capabilities and weapon systems deny their ability to communicate, track, or target. EW also supports fires by enabling lethal fires through the employment of ES to search for, identify, and locate or localize sources of radiated electromagnetic energy used by the enemy for targeting. Defensive EA can support fires through the deployment of decoys or noise to mask friendly fires networks.

SUSTAINMENT

1-67.   Cyberspace operations support sustainment through DODIN operations and defensive cyberspace operations (DCO). Sustainment organizations, functions, systems, and sustainment locations that are highly dependent on DODIN operations include—
- The global supply chain.
- Army logistics networks and information systems.
- Mobilization and power projection platforms.
- Aerial ports of debarkation.
- Seaports of debarkation.

1-68.   DODIN operations establish the necessary communications to conduct sustainment functions. Cyberspace forces defend sustainment systems when adversaries breach cybersecurity measures of networks and systems from threat cyberspace attacks. EW supports sustainment through EP and ES, ensuring freedom of action for DODIN operations in and through the EMS for continued sustainment support. Management, coordination, and deconfliction of frequencies in the EMS are functions of spectrum management operations. Refer to Chapter 2 for more information on defensive cyberspace operations-internal defensive measures (DCO-IDM).

PROTECTION

1-69.   DCO-IDM and EP tasks, in addition to the cyberspace security tasks of DODIN operations, are part of the protection warfighting function. DODIN operations, DCO-IDM, EP, and defensive EA support protection by securing and defending the DODIN-A. Cyberspace forces conduct DCO-IDM to detect, characterize, counter, and mitigate ongoing or imminent threats to the DODIN-A. DODIN operations and DCO-IDM also enable other protection tasks by providing secured communications for—
- Area security.
- Police operations.
- Personnel recovery.
- Air and missile defense.
- Detention operations.

1-70.   EP involves actions to protect personnel, facilities, and equipment from friendly, neutral, or enemy use of the EMS. EP includes measures to protect friendly personnel and equipment in a contested and congested electromagnetic operational environment (EMOE). The EMOE is a composite of the actual and potential electromagnetic energy radiation, conditions, circumstances, and influences that affect the employment of capabilities and the decisions of the commander. The CEMA spectrum manager work closely with the S-6 or G-6 spectrum manager to deconflict frequencies used by friendly forces. Friendly forces can employ proactive measures such as emission control to reduce their electromagnetic signature, thus increasing OPSEC. Defensive EA protects friendly forces by denying enemy use of the EMS, disrupting their ability to target, guide, or fire weapons. Refer to Chapters 2 and 4 of this publication for more information on emission control.

Other titles we publish on Amazon.com:

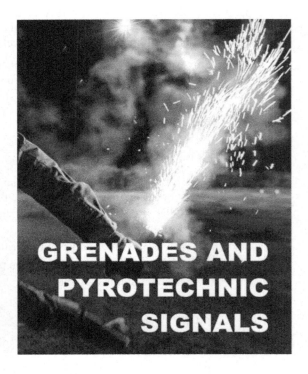

Chapter 2

Cyberspace Operations and Electromagnetic Warfare Fundamentals

This chapter describes the types of cyberspace operations and electromagnetic warfare and associated tasks. It details common effects that commanders can achieve through cyberspace operations and electromagnetic warfare, and discusses the interrelationship between cyberspace operations and electromagnetic warfare and other Army operations. This chapter also discusses training used to prepare Soldiers to execute cyberspace operations and electromagnetic warfare missions.

SECTION I – CYBERSPACE OPERATIONS

2-1.   Cyberspace operations and EW can benefit from synchronization with other Army capabilities using a combined arms approach to achieve objectives against enemy forces. Cyberspace operations and EW can provide commanders with positions of relative advantage in the multi-domain fight. Effects that bleed over from the cyberspace domain into the physical domain can be generated and leveraged against the adversary. A *cyberspace capability* is a device or computer program, including any combination of software, firmware, or hardware, designed to create an effect in or through cyberspace (JP 3-12).

> *Note.* Law enforcement and counterintelligence capabilities may create effects in cyberspace during their efforts to disrupt, destroy, deny, or degrade an enemy or adversary's activities in cyberspace.

2-2.   *Electromagnetic spectrum superiority* is the degree of control in the electromagnetic spectrum that permits the conduct of operations at a given time and place without prohibitive interference, while affecting the threat's ability to do the same (JP 3-85). EW creates effects in the EMS and enables commanders to gain EMS superiority while conducting Army operations. EW capabilities consist of the systems and weapons used to conduct EW missions to create lethal and non-lethal effects in and through the EMS.

Russia's Application of Cyberspace Operations and Electronic Warfare during the Russo-Ukrainian War

In 2013, Ukraine's pro-Russian leadership opted for closer ties to the pro-Russian Eurasian Economic Union rather than sign with the European Union. In response, violent protests erupted throughout Ukraine. In constant competition with the United States and China to increase the flow of trade, Russia has always sought access in expanding commerce throughout the region. As Ukraine descended into chaos, Vladimir Putin and the Russian Federation recognized conditions were optimal for seizure of Ukraine's Black Sea warm water ports in the Crimea. Seizure of these ports not only provided lucrative access to Mediterranean trade and commerce, but also challenged the United States' military power on the Black Sea. Russian actions also included strategic efforts to stop NATO expansion and to reduce the buffer zone between the west and Russian economic expansion.

Ukraine's use of Russian command, control, communications, computer, surveillance, and reconnaissance (C4ISR) made them vulnerable to Russian exploitation and attacks. Formulating their campaign plans around thematic denial and deception operations, Russian military planners went to work on a hybrid campaign that was a multifaceted mix of regular and irregular actions. Russian planners identified Ukraine's center of gravity as their C4ISR. Russia infiltrated Ukrainian telecommunication systems, while Ukrainian's use of communication devices likely aided Russia's targeting efforts. In order to inject strategic, operational, and tactical chaos within Ukraine's decision-making cycle, Russia conducted targeted cyberspace operations and electromagnetic warfare (denial of service, manipulation of social media, etc.) on critical C4ISR nodes. At the tactical level, the Russian Army's utilization of targeted cyberspace and electromagnetic warfare actions were lethal.

The Ukrainian Army moved several mechanized brigades near the Russian border in order to interdict illegal cross border shipments of equipment heading to rebels in Eastern Ukraine. On the morning of 11 July 2014, Ukrainian soldiers spotted a drone orbiting above them. Shortly after the drone disappeared, one of the Ukrainian brigades was struck with a devastating barrage from a 9A52-4 Tornado multiple rocket system.

Rockets containing a mixture of high explosive, cluster, and thermobaric munitions rained down on the unit's positions over the course of four minutes. Following this initial rocket salvo, the Russians followed with high explosive artillery rounds and the cumulative effects were devastating. In a post mortem of the action, the Ukrainian Army suffered 37 killed and 100 wounded. One Ukrainian battalion was virtually destroyed, and others were rendered combat ineffective due to heavy losses in personnel and equipment. It was later assessed that the Russian Army's ability to collect intelligence and geo-locate, coupled with their ability to target Ukrainian communication nodes, played a significant role in enabling the Russians to find, fix, and destroy an entire Ukrainian combat arms brigade. The Russians' targeted application of electromagnetic warfare and cyber attacks created chaos within Ukraine's civil and military leadership and left them confused, a second-order effect. Western leaders found themselves limited in their ability to respond to Russian actions in the region. Russia's use of cyberspace and electromagnetic warfare capabilities to Ukraine's command and control enabled them the seize Crimea and achieve their strategic goal of obtaining commercial and military ports on the Black Sea.

JOINT FORCE AND ARMY

2-3.   The joint force and the Army divide cyberspace operations into three categories based on the portion of cyberspace in which the operations take place and the type of cyberspace forces that conduct those operations. Each of type of cyberspace operation has varying associated authorities, approval levels, and coordination considerations. An Army taxonomy of cyberspace operations is depicted in figure 2-1, below. The three types of cyberspace operations are—

- DODIN operations (refer to ATP 6-02.71).
- DCO.
- OCO.

2-4.   The Army conducts DODIN operations on internal Army and DOD networks and systems using primarily signal forces. The Army employs cyberspace forces to conduct DCO which includes two further sub-divisions—DCO-IDM and defensive cyberspace operations-response actions (DCO-RA). Cyberspace forces conduct DCO-IDM within the DODIN boundary, or on other friendly networks when authorized, in order to defend those networks from imminent or ongoing attacks. At times cyberspace forces may also take action against threat cyberspace actors in neutral or adversary networks in defense of the DODIN or friendly networks. These types of actions, called DCO-RA, require additional authorities and coordination measures. Lastly, cyberspace forces deliberately target threat capabilities in neutral, adversary, and enemy-held portions of cyberspace by conducting OCO. Cyberspace forces may include joint forces from the DOD cyber mission forces or Army-retained cyberspace forces. See Chapter 3 of this publication for more details on cyberspace forces.

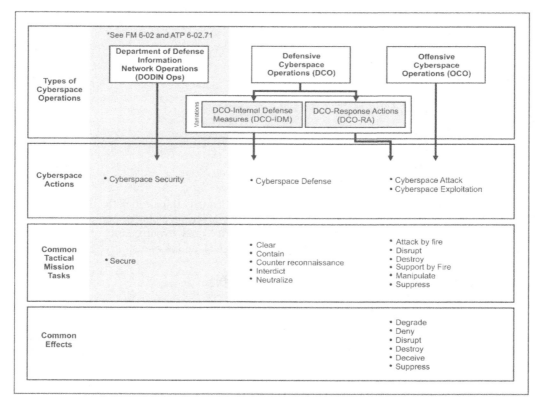

Figure 2-1. Cyberspace operations taxonomy

DEPARTMENT OF DEFENSE INFORMATION NETWORK OPERATIONS

2-5.   The *Department of Defense information network* is the set of information capabilities and associated processes for collecting, processing, storing, disseminating, and managing information on demand to warfighters, policy makers, and support personnel, whether interconnected or stand-alone. Also called DODIN (JP 6-0). This includes owned and leased communications and computing systems and services, software (including applications), data, security services, other associated services, and national security systems. *Department of Defense information network operations* are operations to secure, configure, operate, extend, maintain, and sustain Department of Defense cyberspace to create and preserve the confidentiality, availability, and integrity of the Department of Defense information network. Also called DODIN operations (JP 3-12). DODIN operations provide authorized users at all echelons with secure, reliable end-to-end network and information system availability. DODIN operations allow commanders to effectively communicate, collaborate, share, manage, and disseminate information using information technology systems.

2-6.   Signal forces install tactical networks, conduct maintenance and sustainment activities, and security evaluation and testing. Signal forces performing DODIN operations may also conduct limited DCO-IDM. Since both cyberspace security and defense tasks are ongoing, standing orders for DODIN operations and DCO-IDM cover most cyberspace security and initial cyberspace defense tasks.

2-7.   The Army secures the DODIN-A using a layered defense approach. Layered defense uses multiple physical, policy, and technical controls in to guard against threats on the network. Layering integrates people, technology, and operational capabilities to establish security barriers across multiple layers of the DODIN-A. Various types of security barriers include—

- Antivirus software.
- Firewalls.
- Anti-spam software.
- Communications security.
- Data encryption.
- Password protection.
- Physical and technical barriers.
- Continuous security training.
- Continuous network monitoring.

2-8.   Security barriers are protective measures against acts that may impair the effectiveness of the network, and therefore the mission command system. Additionally, layering includes perimeter security, enclave security, host security, physical security, personnel security, and cybersecurity policies and standards. Layering protects the cyberspace domain at the physical, logical, and administrative control levels.

DEFENSIVE CYBERSPACE OPERATIONS

2-9.   *Defensive cyberspace operations* are missions to preserve the ability to utilize blue cyberspace capabilities and protect data, networks, cyberspace-enabled devices, and other designated systems by defeating on-going or imminent malicious cyberspace activity (JP 3-12). The term blue cyberspace denotes areas in cyberspace protected by the United States, its mission partners, and other areas the Department of Defense may be ordered to protect. DCO are further categorized based on the location of the actions in cyberspace as—

- DCO-IDM.
- DCO-RA.

DEFENSIVE CYBERSPACE OPERATIONS-INTERNAL DEFENSIVE MEASURES

2-10.   *Defensive cyberspace operations-internal defensive measures* are operations in which authorized defense actions occur within the defended portion of cyberspace (JP 3-12). DCO-IDM is conducted within friendly cyberspace. DCO-IDM involves actions to locate and eliminate cyber threats within friendly networks. Cyberspace forces employ defensive measures to neutralize and eliminate threats, allowing reestablishment of degraded, compromised, or threatened portions of the DODIN. Cyberspace forces conducting DCO-IDM primarily conduct cyberspace defense tasks, but may also perform some tasks similar to cyberspace security.

2-11. *Cyberspace defense* includes actions taken within protected cyberspace to defeat specific threats that have breached or are threatening to breach cyberspace security measures and include actions to detect, characterize, counter, and mitigate threats, including malware or the unauthorized activities of users, and to restore the system to a secure configuration. (JP 3-12). Cyberspace forces act on cues from cybersecurity or intelligence alerts of adversary activity within friendly networks. Cyberspace defense tasks during DCO-IDM include hunting for threats on friendly networks, deploying advanced countermeasures, and responding to eliminate these threats and mitigate their effects.

DEFENSIVE CYBERSPACE OPERATIONS-RESPONSE ACTIONS

2-12. *Defensive cyberspace operation-response actions* are operations that are part of a defensive cyberspace operations mission that are taken external to the defended network or portion of cyberspace without permission of the owner of the affected system (JP 3-12). DCO-RA take place outside the boundary of the DODIN. Some DCO-RA may include actions that rise to the level of use of force and may include physical damage or destruction of enemy systems. DCO-RA consist of conducting cyberspace attacks and cyberspace exploitation similar to OCO. However, DCO-RA use these actions for defensive purposes only, unlike OCO that is used to project power in and through cyberspace.

2-13. Decisions to conduct DCO-RA depend heavily on the broader strategic and operational contexts such as the existence or imminence of open hostilities, the degree of certainty in attribution of the threat; the damage the threat has or is expected to cause, and national policy considerations. DCO-RA are conducted by national mission team(s) and require a properly coordinated military order, coordination with interagency and unified action partners, and careful consideration of scope, rules of engagement, and operational objectives.

OFFENSIVE CYBERSPACE OPERATIONS

2-14. *Offensive cyberspace operations* are missions intended to project power in and through cyberspace (JP 3-12). Cyberspace forces conduct OCO outside of DOD networks to achieve positions of relative advantage through cyberspace exploitation and cyberspace attack actions in support of commanders' objectives. Commanders must integrate OCO within the combined arms scheme of maneuver throughout the operations process to achieve optimal effects.

2-15. The Army provides cyberspace forces trained to perform OCO across the range of military operations to the joint force. Army forces conducting OCO do so under the authority of a joint force commander. Refer to Appendix C for information on integrating with unified action partners. Joint forces may provide OCO support to corps and below Army commanders in response to requests through the joint targeting process. Refer to Appendix D for more information on joint cyberspace forces. Targets for cyberspace effects may require extended planning time, extended approval time, as well as synchronization and deconfliction with partners external to the DOD. Chapter 4 covers targeting considerations in detail.

CYBERSPACE ACTIONS

2-16. Execution of these cyberspace operations entails one or more specific tasks, which joint cyberspace doctrine refers to as cyberspace actions (refer to JP 3-12), and the employment of one or more cyberspace capabilities. Figure 2-2 on page 2-6 depicts the relationships between the types of cyberspace operations and their associated actions, the location of those operations in cyberspace, and the forces that conduct those operations. The four cyberspace actions are—

- Cyberspace security (refer to FM 6-02 and ATP 6-02.71).
- Cyberspace defense.
- Cyberspace exploitation.

- Cyberspace attack.

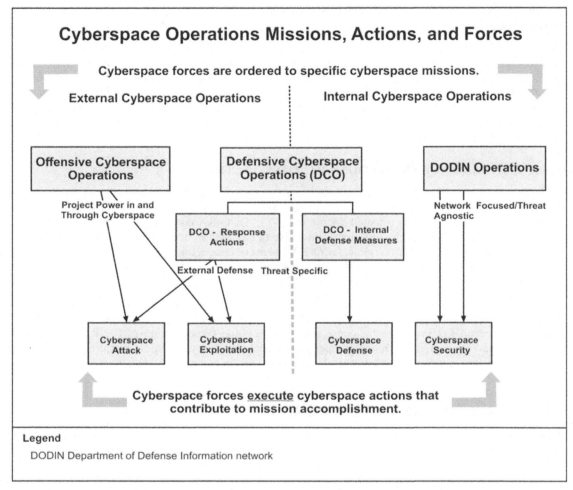

Figure 2-2. Cyberspace operations missions and actions

CYBERSPACE SECURITY

2-17. *Cyberspace security* is actions taken within protected cyberspace to prevent unauthorized access to, exploitation of, or damage to computers, electronic communications systems, and other information technology, including platform information technology, as well as the information contained therein, to ensure its availability, integrity, authentication, confidentiality, and nonrepudiation (JP 3-12). These preventive measures include protecting the information on the DODIN, ensuring the information's availability, integrity, authenticity, confidentiality, and nonrepudiation. Cyberspace security is generally preventative in nature, but also continues throughout DCO-IDM and incident responses in instances where a cyberspace threat compromises the DODIN. Some common types of cyberspace security actions include—

- Password management.
- Software patching.
- Encryption of storage devices.
- Mandatory cybersecurity training for all users.
- Restricting access to suspicious websites.

- Implementing procedures to define the roles, responsibilities, policies, and administrative functions for managing DODIN operations.

2-18. Refer to FM 6-02 for DODIN operations tactics. Refer to ATP 6-02.71 for DODIN operations techniques.

CYBERSPACE EXPLOITATION

2-19. *Cyberspace exploitation* consists of actions taken in cyberspace to gain intelligence, maneuver, collect information, or perform other enabling actions required to prepare for future military operations (JP 3-12). These operations must be authorized through mission orders and are part of OCO or DCO-RA actions in gray or red cyberspace that do not create cyberspace attack effects, and are often intended to remain clandestine. Cyberspace exploitation includes activities to support operational preparation of the environment for current and future operations by gaining and maintaining access to networks, systems, and nodes of military value; maneuvering to positions of advantage within cyberspace; and positioning cyberspace capabilities to facilitate follow-on actions. Cyberspace exploitation actions are deconflicted with other United States Government departments and agencies in accordance with national policy.

CYBERSPACE ATTACK

2-20. *Cyberspace attack* actions taken in cyberspace that create noticeable denial effects (i.e., degradation, disruption, or destruction) in cyberspace or manipulation that leads to denial effects in the physical domains (JP 3-12). A cyberspace attack creates effects in and through cyberspace and may result in physical destruction. Modification or destruction of cyberspace capabilities that control physical processes can lead to effects in the physical domains. Some illustrative examples of common effects created by a cyberspace attack include—

- Deny. To prevent access to, operation of, or availability of a target function by a specified level for a specified time (JP 3-12). Cyberspace attacks deny the enemy's ability to access cyberspace by hindering hardware and software functionalities for a specific duration of time.
- Degrade. To deny access to, or operation of, a target to a level represented as a percentage of capacity. Level of degradation is specified. If a specific time is required, it can be specified (JP 3-12).
- Disrupt. To completely but temporarily deny access to, or operation of, a target for a period of time. A desired start and stop time are normally specified. Disruption can be considered a special case of degradation where the degradation level is 100 percent (JP 3-12). Commanders can use cyberspace attacks that temporarily but completely deny an enemy's ability to access cyberspace or communication links to disrupt decision making, ability to organize formations, and conduct command and control. Disruption effects in cyberspace are usually limited in duration.
- Destroy. To completely and irreparably deny access to, or operation of, a target. Destruction maximizes the time and amount of denial. However, destruction is scoped according to the span of a conflict, since many targets, given enough time and resources, can be reconstituted (JP 3-12). Commanders can use cyberspace attacks to destroy hardware and software beyond repair where replacement is required to restore system function. Destruction of enemy cyberspace capabilities could include irreversible corruption to system software causing loss of data and information, or irreparable damage to hardware such as the computer processor, hard drive, or power supply on a system or systems on the enemy's network.
- Manipulate. Manipulation, as a form of cyberspace attack, controls or changes information, information systems, and/or networks in gray or red cyberspace to create physical denial effects, using deception, decoying, conditioning, spoofing, falsification, and other similar techniques. It uses an adversary's information resources for friendly purposes, to create denial effects not immediately apparent in cyberspace (JP 3-12). Commanders can use cyberspace attacks to manipulate enemy information or information systems in support of tactical deception objectives or as part of joint military deception. Refer to FM 3-13.4 for information on Army support to military deception.

Note. Cyberspace attacks are types of fires conducted during DCO-RA and OCO actions and are limited to cyber mission force(s) engagement. They require coordination with other United States Government departments and agencies and careful synchronization with other lethal and non-lethal effects through established targeting processes.

SECTION II – ELECTROMAGNETIC WARFARE

2-21. Modern militaries rely on communications equipment using broad portions of the EMS to conduct military operations allowing forces to talk, transmit data, and provide navigation and timing information, and command and control troops worldwide. They also rely on the EMS for sensing and awareness of the OE. The Army conducts EW to gain and maintain positions of relative advantage within the EMS. The Army's contribution to electromagnetic spectrum operations is accomplished by integrating and synchronizing EW and spectrum management operations. EW refers to military actions involving the use of electromagnetic and directed energy to control the EMS or to attack the enemy. EW consists of three distinct divisions: EA, EP, and ES. These divisions often mutually support each other in operations. For example, radar-jamming EA can serve a protection function for friendly forces to penetrate defended airspace; it can also prevent an adversary from having a complete operating picture. Figure 2-3 illustrates the EW taxonomy.

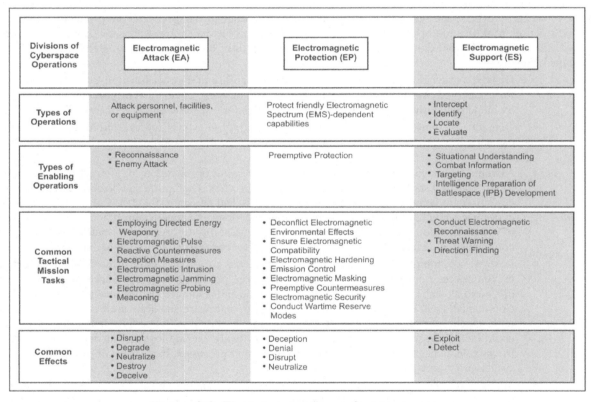

Figure 2-3. Electromagnetic warfare taxonomy

ELECTROMAGNETIC ATTACK

2-22. Army forces conduct both offensive and defensive EA to fulfill the commander's objectives in support of the mission. EA projects power in and through the EMS by implementing active and passive actions to deny enemy capabilities and equipment, or by employing passive systems to protect friendly capabilities. *Electromagnetic attack* is a division of electromagnetic warfare involving the use of electromagnetic energy, directed energy, or antiradiation weapons to attack personnel, facilities, or equipment with the intent of degrading, neutralizing, or destroying enemy combat capability and considered a form of fires (JP 3-85). EA requires systems or weapons that radiate electromagnetic energy as active measures and systems that do not radiate or re-radiate electromagnetic energy as passive measures.

2-23. Offensive EA prevents or reduces an enemy's effective use of the EMS by employing jamming and directed energy weapon systems against enemy spectrum-dependent systems and devices. Offensive EA systems and capabilities include—

- Jammers.
- Directed energy weaponry.
- Self-propelled decoys.
- Electromagnetic deception.
- Antiradiation missiles.

2-24. Defensive EA protects against lethal attacks by denying enemy use of the EMS to target, guide, and trigger weapons that negatively impact friendly systems. Defensive EA supports force protection, self-protection and OPSEC efforts by degrading, neutralizing, or destroying an enemy's surveillance capabilities against protected units. Defensive EA systems and capabilities include—

- Expendables (flares and active decoys).
- Jammers.
- Towed decoys.
- Directed energy infrared countermeasure systems.
- Radio controlled improvised explosive device (RCIED) systems.
- Counter Unmanned Aerial Systems (C-UAS).

2-25. EA effects available to the commander include—

- **Destroy**. Destruction makes the condition of a target so damaged that it can neither function nor be restored to a usable condition in a timeframe relevant to the current operation. When used in the EW context, destruction is the use of EA to eliminate targeted enemy personnel, facilities, or equipment (JP 3-85).
- **Degrade**. Degradation reduces the effectiveness or efficiency of an enemy EMS-dependent system. The impact of degradation may last a few seconds or remain throughout the entire operation (JP 3-85).
- **Disrupt**. Disruption temporarily interrupts the operation of an enemy EMS dependent system (JP 3-85).
- **Deceive**. Deception measures are designed to mislead the enemy by manipulation, distortion, or falsification of evidence to induce them to react in a manner prejudicial to their interests. Deception in an EW context presents enemy operators and higher-level processing functions with erroneous inputs, either directly through the sensors themselves or through EMS-based networks such as voice communications or data links (JP 3-85).

ELECTROMAGNETIC ATTACK TASKS

2-26. EA has the unique potential to affect enemy use of the EMS and attack the enemy through the EMS. Other offensive options can affect enemy use of the EMS but are likely to cause collateral damage outside the EMS, whereas EA uses the EMS for its effects. Concurrently, EA's potential to cause EMS fratricide necessitates caution and coordination in its employment.

2-27. EA tasks include—

- Employing directed energy weaponry.
- Electromagnetic pulse.
- Reactive countermeasures.
- Deception measures.
- Electromagnetic intrusion.

- Electromagnetic jamming.
- Electromagnetic probing.
- Meaconing.

Directed Energy

2-28. *Directed energy* is an umbrella term covering technologies that relate to the production of a beam of concentrated electromagnetic energy or atomic or subatomic particles. (JP 3-85). Directed energy becomes a directed energy weapon when used to conduct EA. A *directed-energy weapon* is a weapon or system that uses directed energy to incapacitate, damage, or destroy enemy equipment, facilities, and/or personnel (JP 3-85). EA involving the use of directed-energy weapons is called directed-energy warfare. *Directed-energy warfare* is military action involving the use of directed-energy weapons, devices, and countermeasures (JP 3-85). The purpose of directed-energy warfare is to disable, cause direct damage, or destroy enemy equipment, facilities, or personnel. Another use for directed-energy warfare is to determine, exploit, reduce, or prevent hostile use of the EMS by neutralization or destruction.

Electromagnetic Pulse

2-29. *Electromagnetic pulse* is a strong burst of electromagnetic radiation caused by a nuclear explosion, energy weapon, or by natural phenomenon, that may couple with electrical or electronic systems to produce damaging current and voltage surges (JP 3-85). The effects of an electromagnetic pulse can extend hundreds of kilometers depending on the height and power output of the electromagnetic pulse burst. A high-altitude electromagnetic pulse can generate destructive effects over a continent-sized area. The most affected portion of the EMS by electromagnetic pulse or high-altitude electromagnetic pulse is the radio spectrum. Electromagnetic energy produced by an electromagnetic pulse excludes the highest frequencies of the optical (infrared, visible, ultraviolet) and ionizing (X and gamma rays) ranges. An indirect impact of an electromagnetic pulse or high-altitude electromagnetic pulse includes electrical fires caused by the overheating of electrical systems and components.

Reactive Countermeasures

2-30. EA includes reactive countermeasures as a response to an enemy attack in the EMS. Response to enemy attack may include employing radio frequency countermeasures, such as flares and chaff, in disrupting enemy systems and weapons, such as precision-guided or radio-controlled weapons, communications equipment, and sensor systems. *Radio frequency countermeasures* are any device or technique employing radio frequency materials or technology that is intended to impair the effectiveness of enemy activity, particularly with respect to precision guided and sensor systems (JP 3-85). *Chaff* is radar confusion reflectors, consisting of thin, narrow metallic strips of various lengths and frequency responses, which are used to reflect echoes for confusion purposes (JP 3-85). Reactive countermeasures may provoke the employment of directed energy weaponry or electromagnetic pulse and can include the use of lethal fires. Army forces can disrupt enemy guided weapons and sensor systems by deploying passive and active electro-optical-infrared countermeasures that include—

- Smokes.
- Aerosols.
- Signature suppressants.
- Decoys.
- Pyrotechnics.
- Pyrophoric.
- Laser jammers.
- High-energy lasers
- Directed infrared energy.

Deception Measures

2-31. Deception measures are designed to mislead the enemy by manipulation, distortion, or falsification of evidence to induce them to react in a manner prejudicial to their interests. Electromagnetic deception uses misleading information by injecting false data into the adversary's EMS-dependent voice and data networks to inhibit the effectiveness of intelligence, surveillance, and reconnaissance sensor systems. EW uses the EMS to deceive a threat's decision loop, making it difficult to establish an accurate perception of Army forces' objective reality. EW supports all deceptions plans, both Joint military deception and tactical deception, using electromagnetic deception measures and scaling appropriately for the desired effect. Electromagnetic deception measures provide misleading signals in electromagnetic energy, for example by injecting false signals into a threat's sensor systems such as radar. Commander's authority to plan and execute deception integrated with electromagnetic deception measures may be limited by separate EW authorities and rules of engagement (Technical means for deception are in CJCSI 3211.01F and AR 525-21).

Electromagnetic Intrusion

2-32. *Electromagnetic intrusion* is the intentional insertion of electromagnetic energy into transmission paths in any manner, with the objective of deceiving operators or of causing confusion (JP 3-85). An example of electromagnetic intrusion is injecting false or misleading information into an enemy's radio communications, acting as the enemy's higher headquarters. Electromagnetic intrusion can also create deception or confusion in a threat aircraft's intelligent flight control system, compromising the intelligent flight control system' neural network and the pilot's ability to maintain control.

Electromagnetic Jamming

2-33. *Electromagnetic jamming* is the deliberate radiation, reradiation, or reflection of electromagnetic energy for the purpose of preventing or reducing an enemy's effective use of the electromagnetic spectrum, with the intent of degrading or neutralizing the enemy's combat capability (JP 3-85). Targets subjected to jamming may include radios, navigational systems, radars, and satellites. Electromagnetic jamming can disrupt a threat aircraft's intelligent flight control system by jamming its sensors, denying its ability to obtain navigational or altitude data crucial to flight performance. Electromagnetic jamming can also prevent or reduce the effectiveness of an enemy's integrated air defense system by jamming its anti-aircraft sensors used for targeting.

Electromagnetic Probing

2-34. *Electromagnetic probing* is the intentional radiation designed to be introduced into the devices or systems of an adversary for the purpose of learning the functions and operational capabilities of the devices or systems (JP 3-85). Electromagnetic probing involves accessing an enemy's spectrum-dependent devices to obtain information about the targeted devices' functions, capabilities, and purpose. Electromagnetic probing may provide information about threat capabilities and their ability to affect or detect friendly operations. Army forces may conduct overt electromagnetic probing to elicit a response from an enemy, exposing their location.

Meaconing

2-35. Meaconing consists of receiving radio beacon signals and rebroadcasting them on the same frequency to confuse navigation. Meaconing stations cause inaccurate bearings to be obtained by aircraft or ground stations (JP 3-85).

ELECTROMAGNETIC PROTECTION

2-36. *Electromagnetic protection* is the division of electromagnetic warfare involving actions taken to protect personnel, facilities, and equipment from any effects of friendly, neutral, or enemy use of the electromagnetic spectrum that degrade, neutralize, or destroy friendly combat capability (JP 3-85). EP measures eliminate or mitigate the negative impact resulting from friendly, neutral, enemy, or naturally occurring EMI.

2-37. Both EP and defensive EA can have protective effects. However, EP focuses explicitly on protecting friendly EMS-dependent capabilities. In contrast, the protective effects of defensive EA focus on attacking enemy capabilities that support their opposition to friendly forces and operations. EP includes protective measures for friendly forces operating near or handling live ordnance by preventing inadvertent detonations due to electromagnetic energy.

ELECTROMAGNETIC PROTECTION TASKS

2-38. Adversaries are heavily invested in diminishing our effective use of the electromagnetic spectrum. It is crucial we understand the enemy threat and our vulnerabilities to our systems, equipment and personnel. Effective EP measures will minimize natural phenomena and mitigate the enemy's ability to conduct ES and EA actions against friendly forces successfully.

2-39. EP tasks include—
- Electromagnetic environmental effects deconfliction.
- Electromagnetic compatibility.
- Electromagnetic hardening.
- Emission control.
- Electromagnetic masking.
- Preemptive countermeasures.
- Electromagnetic security.
- Wartime reserve modes.

Electromagnetic Environmental Effects Deconfliction

2-40. *Electromagnetic vulnerability* is the characteristics of a system that cause it to suffer a definite degradation (incapability to perform the designated mission) as a result of having been subjected to a certain level of electromagnetic environmental effects (JP 3-85). Any system operating in the EMS is susceptible to electromagnetic environmental effects. Any spectrum-dependent device exposed to or having electromagnetic compatibility issues within an EMOE may result in the increased potential for such electromagnetic vulnerability as safety, interoperability, and reliability issues. Electromagnetic vulnerability manifests when spectrum-dependent devices suffer levels of degradation that render them incapable of performing operations when subjected to electromagnetic environmental effects.

2-41. Electromagnetic compatibility, EMS deconfliction, electromagnetic pulse, and EMI mitigation reduce the impact of electromagnetic environmental effects. Recognizing the different types of electromagnetic radiation hazards allows planners to use appropriate measures to counter or mitigate electromagnetic environmental effects. Electromagnetic radiation hazards include— hazards of electromagnetic radiation to personnel, hazards of electromagnetic radiation to ordnance, and hazards of electromagnetic radiation to fuels. Electromagnetic environmental effects can also occur from natural phenomena such as lightning and precipitation static.

Electromagnetic Compatibility

2-42. *Electromagnetic compatibility* is the ability of systems, equipment, and devices that use the electromagnetic spectrum to operate in their intended environments without causing or suffering unacceptable or unintentional degradation because of electromagnetic radiation or response (JP 3-85). The CEMA spectrum manager assists the G-6 or S-6 spectrum manager with implementing electromagnetic compatibility to mitigate electromagnetic vulnerabilities by applying sound spectrum planning, coordination, and management of the EMS. Operational forces have minimal ability to mitigate electromagnetic compatibility issues. Instead, they must document identified electromagnetic compatibility issues so that the Service component program management offices may coordinate the required changes necessary to reduce compatibility issues.

Electromagnetic Hardening

2-43. *Electromagnetic hardening* consists of actions taken to protect personnel, facilities, and/or equipment by blanking, filtering, attenuating, grounding, bonding, and/or shielding against undesirable effects of electromagnetic energy (JP 3-85). Electromagnetic hardening can protect friendly spectrum-dependent devices from the impact of EMI or threat EA such as lasers, high-powered microwave, or electromagnetic pulse. An example of electromagnetic hardening includes installing electromagnetic conduit consisting of conductive or magnetic materials to shield against undesirable effects of electromagnetic energy.

Emission Control

2-44. *Emission control* is the selective and controlled use of electromagnetic, acoustic, or other emitters to optimize command and control capabilities while minimizing, for operations security: a. detection by enemy sensors, b. mutual interference among friendly systems, and/or c. enemy interference with the ability to execute a military deception plan (JP 3-85). emission control enables OPSEC by—

- Decreasing detection probability and countering detection range by enemy sensors.
- Identifying and mitigating EMI among friendly spectrum-dependent devices
- Identifying enemy EMI that allows execution of military deception planning.

2-45. Emission control enables electromagnetic masking by integrating intelligence, and EW to adjust spectrum management and communications plans. A practical and disciplined emission control plan, in conjunction with other EP measures, is a critical aspect of good OPSEC. Refer to ATP 3-13.3 for OPSEC techniques at division and below.

Electromagnetic Masking

2-46. *Electromagnetic masking* is the controlled radiation of electromagnetic energy on friendly frequencies in a manner to protect the emissions of friendly communications and electronic systems against enemy electromagnetic support measures/signals intelligence without significantly degrading the operation of friendly systems (JP 3-85). Electromagnetic masking disguises, distorts, or manipulates friendly electromagnetic radiation to conceal military operations information or present false perceptions to adversary commanders. Electromagnetic masking is an essential component of military deception, OPSEC, and signals security.

Preemptive Countermeasures

2-47. *Countermeasures* consist of that form of military science that, by the employment of devices and/or techniques, has as its objective the impairment of the operational effectiveness of enemy activity (JP 3-85). Countermeasures can be passive (non-radiating or reradiating electromagnetic energy) or active (radiating electromagnetic energy) and deployed preemptively or reactively. Preemptive deployment of passive countermeasures are precautionary procedures to disrupt an enemy attack in the EMS through the use of passive devices such as chaff which reradiates, or the use of radio frequency absorptive material which impedes the return of the radio frequency signal.

Electromagnetic Security

2-48. *Electromagnetic security* is the protection resulting from all measures designed to deny unauthorized persons information of value that might be derived from their interception and study of noncommunications electromagnetic radiation (e.g., radar) (JP 3-85). Changing the modulation and characteristics of electromagnetic frequencies used for radars make it difficult for a threat to intercept and study radar signals.

Wartime Reserve Modes

2-49. *Wartime reserve modes* are characteristics and operating procedures of sensor, communications, navigation aids, threat recognition, weapons, and countermeasure systems that will contribute to military effectiveness if unknown to or misunderstood by opposing commanders before they are used, but could be exploited or neutralized if known in advance (JP 3-85). Wartime reserve modes are held deliberately in reserve for wartime or emergency use.

ELECTROMAGNETIC SUPPORT

2-50. *Electromagnetic support* refers to the division of electromagnetic warfare involving actions tasked by, or under the direct control of, an operational commander to search for, intercept, identify, and locate or localize sources of intentional and unintentional radiated electromagnetic energy for immediate threat recognition, targeting, planning, and conduct of future operations (JP 3-85). In multi-domain operations, commanders work to dominate the EMS and shape the operational environment by detecting, intercepting, analyzing, identifying, locating, and affecting (deny, degrade, disrupt, deceive, destroy, and manipulate) adversary electromagnetic systems that support military operations. Simultaneously, they also work to protect and enable U.S. and Allied forces' freedom of action in and through the EMS.

2-51. The purpose of ES is to acquire adversary combat information in support of a commander's maneuver plan. *Combat information* is unevaluated data, gathered by or provided directly to the tactical commander which, due to its highly perishable nature or the criticality of the situation, cannot be processed into tactical intelligence in time to satisfy the user's tactical intelligence requirements (JP 2-01). Combat information used for planning or conducting combat operations, to include EA missions, is acquired under Command authority; however, partner nation privacy concerns must be taken into account. Decryption of communications is an exclusively SIGINT function and may only be performed by SIGINT personnel operating under Director, National Security Agency and Chief, National Security Service SIGINT operational control (DODI O-3115.07).

2-52. ES supports operations by obtaining EMS-derived combat information to enable effects and planning. Combat information is collected for immediate use in support of threat recognition, current operations, targeting for EA or lethal attacks, and support the commander's planning of future operations. Data collected through ES can also support SIGINT processing, exploitation, and dissemination to support the commander's intelligence and targeting requirements and provide situational understanding. Data and information obtained through ES depend on the timely collection, processing, and reporting to alert the commander and staff of potential critical combat information.

ELECTROMAGNETIC SUPPORT TASKS

2-53. When conducting electromagnetic support, commanders employ EW platoons located in the brigade, combat team (BCT) military intelligence company (MICO) to support with information collection efforts, survey of the EMS, integration and multisource analysis by providing indications and warning, radio frequency direction finding and geolocation of threat emissions.

2-54. ES tasks include—

- Electromagnetic Reconnaissance.
- Threat Warning.
- Direction finding.

Electromagnetic Reconnaissance

2-55. *Electromagnetic reconnaissance* is the detection, location, identification, and evaluation of foreign electromagnetic radiations (energy) (JP 3-85). Electromagnetic reconnaissance is an action used to support information collection and is an element of the tactical task reconnaissance (see Chapter 4). Information obtained through electromagnetic reconnaissance assists the commander with situational understanding and decision making and, can be further processed to support SIGINT activities. Electromagnetic reconnaissance may result in EP modifications or lead to an EA or lethal attack.

2-56. Information obtained through electromagnetic reconnaissance, in conjunction with other sources of information and intelligence data, can be used for precision geolocation. Precision geolocation involves planning, coordinating, and managing friendly assets to geolocate enemy radio frequency systems for targeting. The data gathered is analyzed to determine the location of the electromagnetic energy's origin. This information provides the fires support element with a physical location of enemy systems radiating electromagnetic energy.

Threat Warning

2-57. Threat warning enables the commander and staff to quickly identify immediate threats to friendly forces and implement EA or EP countermeasures. EW personnel employ sensors to detect, intercept, identify, and locate adversary electromagnetic signatures and provides an early warning of an imminent or potential threat. EW personnel coordinate with G-2 or S-2 on the long-term impact of detected enemy emitters. Threat warning assists the commander's decision making process in IPB development, updating electromagnetic order of battle, and assisting in the correlation of enemy emitters to communication and weapon systems.

2-58. Known electromagnetic signatures should be compared against the electromagnetic order of battle, high-value target, and the high-payoff target list and action taken as warranted by current policy or higher guidance. Unknown radiated electromagnetic signatures detected in the EMS are forwarded to the G-2 or S-2 for analysis. The G-2 or S-2 validates known and unknown systems as part of information collection that feeds the operations process. Staffs analyze and report information to higher and subordinate headquarters, to other Army and joint forces, and to unified action partners in the AO.

Direction Finding

2-59. *Direction finding* is a procedure for obtaining bearings of radio frequency emitters by using a highly directional antenna and a display unit on an intercept receiver or ancillary equipment (JP 3-85). EW personnel leverage various ES platforms with direction finding capabilities to locate enemy forces. Multiple direction finding systems are preferred for a greater confidence level of the enemy location. ES platforms are deployed in various formations to create a baseline and increase the area of coverage. Three or more direction finding systems are considered optimal in triangulating the targeted emitter.

ELECTROMAGNETIC SUPPORT AND SIGNALS INTELLIGENCE

2-60. ES and SIGINT often share the same or similar assets and resources, and personnel conducting ES could be required to collect information that meets both requirements simultaneously. SIGINT consists of communications intelligence, electronic intelligence, and foreign instrumentation SIGINT. Commonalities between ES and SIGINT are similar during the early stages of sensing, collecting, identifying, and locating foreign spectrum emissions. The distinction between ES and SIGINT is determined by who has operational control of assets collecting information, what capabilities those assets must provide, and why they are needed. Information and data become SIGINT when cryptologic processes are applied to a signal to determine its relevance, value, or meaning solely for intelligence. There are also delineating hard lines regarding the systems, signal complexity, and reporting timeliness that divide ES and SIGINT. While both ES and SIGINT report information that meets reporting thresholds directly to the supported unit, SIGINT is obligated further to report acquired information through the U.S. SIGINT system. The added requirement for SIGINT provides accountability and enables the greater intelligence community access to the information for additional intelligence production and dissemination as required. For more information on SIGINT, refer to ADP 2-0.

ELECTROMAGNETIC WARFARE REPROGRAMMING

2-61. *Electromagnetic warfare reprogramming* is the deliberate alteration or modification of electromagnetic warfare or target sensing systems, or the tactics and procedures that employ them, in response to validated changes in equipment, tactics, or the electromagnetic environment (JP 3-85). The purpose of EW reprogramming is to maintain or enhance the effectiveness of EW and targeting sensing systems. EW reprogramming includes changes to EW and targeting sensing software (TSS) equipment such as self-defense systems, offensive weapons systems, and intelligence collection systems. EW consists of three distinct divisions: EA, EP, and ES, which are supported by EW reprogramming activities.

2-62. Army forces follow the combatant command (CCMD) joint coordination electromagnetic warfare reprogramming policy and procedures during all training events and operations. Units establish EW reprogramming support programs, and the cyber electromagnetic warfare officer (CEWO) ensures the unit follows joint coordination electromagnetic warfare reprogramming policies and procedures regarding EW reprogramming and maintain awareness of EW reprogramming efforts conducted by other organizations in the AO. See Appendix F for detailed information regarding EW reprogramming.

SECTION III – INTERRELATIONSHIP WITH OTHER OPERATIONS

2-63. This section describes the relationship that cyberspace operations and EW have with other operations. It discusses how cyberspace operations and EW mutually support intelligence operations, space operations, and information operations.

INTELLIGENCE OPERATIONS

2-64. As an operation, *intelligence* is (1) the product resulting from the collection, processing, integration, evaluation, analysis, and interpretation of available information concerning foreign nations, hostile or potentially hostile forces or elements, or areas of actual or potential operations; (2) the activities that result in the production; and (3) the organizations engaged in such activities (JP 2-0). Intelligence at all echelons supports the planning of cyberspace operations and EW and assists with defining measures of performance and effectiveness. Intelligence also assists the fires support element in developing the high payoff target (HPT) list, and collaborating with the CEMA section to ensure the high payoff target list includes enemy cyberspace and EW-related targets. Intelligence also plays a crucial part in assisting the fires support element in continued target development, including forwarding targets to the joint task force (JTF) headquarters for assessment as potential targets for the joint targeting list.

2-65. Information collection supports cyberspace operations and EW by collecting information to satisfy commander's critical information requirement(s) (CCIRs) and staff members' information requirements (IRs) regarding friendly, neutral, and enemy cyberspace and EMS capabilities, activities, disposition, and characteristics within the OE. Information collection also drives capability development. A robust intelligence package is imperative to understanding the target space, developing tools and having meaningful effects in cyberspace. There are four tasks and missions nested in information collection: intelligence operations, reconnaissance, surveillance, and security operations (See Chapter 4).

2-66. Information obtained by information collection drives the IPB process. Through the IPB process, the G-2 or S-2 analyzes operational and mission variables in an area of interest to determine their effect on operations. These variables affect how friendly forces will conduct cyberspace operations and EW within the assigned AO. Conversely, cyberspace operations and EW also contribute to intelligence by supporting information collection. Cyberspace operations and EW capabilities collect combat information to answer CCIRs and IRs for situational awareness and targeting.

2-67. SIGINT, cyberspace operations, and EW may overlap during operations in the EMS. For this reason, effective integration of SIGINT, cyberspace, EW, and spectrum management operations extends well beyond simple coordination. Effective integration requires both deconfliction and identification of windows of opportunity among these operations. This integration requires close staff collaboration, detailed procedural controls, and various technical channels. See Chapter 4 for additional details.

2-68. The intelligence staff also identifies adversary and enemy key terrain as part of the IPB process. Cyberspace operations use the concept of key terrain as a model to identify critical aspects of the cyberspace domain. Identified key terrain in cyberspace is subject to actions the controlling combatant (friendly, enemy, or adversary) deems advantageous such as defending, exploiting, and attacking. Key terrain in cyberspace corresponds to nodes, links, processes, or assets in cyberspace, whether part of the physical, logical, or cyber-persona layer. Key terrain in cyberspace may include—

- Locations in cyberspace in which friendly forces can gather intelligence.
- Locations in cyberspace that support network connectivity.
- Entry points to friendly networks that require priorities for defense.
- Locations in cyberspace that friendly forces require access for essential functions or capabilities.

SPACE OPERATIONS

2-69. Cyberspace and space operations are interdependent. Access to the space domain is critical to cyberspace operations, especially DODIN operations, enabling global end-to-end network connectivity. In the Army, the space domain is only accessible through space operations. Conversely, space capabilities such as navigation warfare, offensive space control, and defensive space control are dependent on operations conducted in space, cyberspace, and the EMS. This interrelationship is critical, and addressing the interdependencies between the three must be managed throughout the operations process.

2-70. Both cyberspace operations and EW can affect space operations. Ground control systems that control satellites rely on networked computers to maintain orbital parameters and direct onboard sensors, particularly to maintain stable orbits; radios transmit computer commands to the satellites. Computer code sent directly to satellites in orbit can potentially allow remote control of the system, preventing others' access to onboard sensors or communications systems. Adversaries could similarly enter ground control systems and issue alternative orders to satellites to move them out of position or shut off critical systems. Because satellites routinely receive commands using radio frequencies, an adversary might attempt to shut off sensors or directly gain control of the spacecraft, rather than trying to issue orders through a ground control system.

2-71. All space operations rely on the EMS for command and control, sensing, and information distribution. The vital nature of space operations in multi-domain operations requires close coordination with other EMS activities associated with spectrum management operations to ensure proper prioritization, integration, synchronization, and deconfliction. The G-2 or S-2 uses information gathered through space-based intelligence, surveillance, and reconnaissance to assist the commander and staff with attaining situational awareness and understanding of the OE.

2-72. *Navigation warfare* is the deliberate defensive and offensive action to assure and prevent positioning, navigation, and timing information through coordinated employment of space, cyberspace, and electromagnetic warfare operations (JP 3-14). A navigation warfare attack denies threat actors a global navigation satellite system through various methods, including OCO, space operations, and EA. Global navigation satellite system is the general term used to describe any space-based system providing positioning, navigation, and timing (PNT) information worldwide (for example, Global Positioning System). Navigation warfare effectiveness requires synchronization of space operations, cyberspace operations, and EW capabilities with lethal and nonlethal attack actions to create desired effects. EW must be synchronized with space operations to understand the impacts of navigation warfare operations, deny adversary access to global navigation satellite system information, and protect friendly spectrum-dependent devices using specific frequencies within the EMS. Refer to FM 3-14 for more information on navigation warfare.

2-73. The space domain consists of three segments: space, link, and ground. The space segment is the operational area corresponding with the space domain and comprises satellites in both geosynchronous and non-geosynchronous Earth orbit. The link segment consists of signals connecting ground and space segments through the EMS. The ground segment consists of ground-based facilities and equipment supporting command and control of space assets, ground-based processing equipment, earth terminals, user equipment, space situational awareness sensors, and the interconnectivity between the facilities and equipment. Earth terminals include all multi-Service ground, shipborne, submarine, and airborne satellite terminals that establish connectivity to the satellites in the space segment. The three space domain segments rely heavily on cyberspace operations to protect networking and information technologies and infrastructures while depending on the EMS to conduct operations between the space, link, and ground segments.

2-74. Cyberspace operations contribute to space operations by protecting friendly networks that leverage the global navigation satellite system while targeting similar enemy and adversary capabilities. Additionally, cyberspace operations establish network connectivity between ground-based facilities and equipment throughout the space domain's ground segment. EW supports navigation warfare by denying the enemy access to global navigation satellite system information while protecting friendly space capabilities operating in the EMS.

2-75. Integrating cyberspace operations, EW, and space operations enable commanders and staffs at each level to synchronize capabilities and effects. Space-based capabilities (space segment) enable distributed and global cyberspace operations. Cyberspace and space-based capabilities provide responsive and timely support that allows commanders to project combat power from the highest echelons down to the tactical level. Synchronization with spectrum management operations is necessary to ensure the availability of resources in the EMS and to prevent spectrum conflicts. Refer to FM 3-14 for more information about space operations.

INFORMATION OPERATIONS

2-76. *Information operations* are the integrated employment, during military operations, of information-related capabilities in concert with other lines of operations to influence, disrupt, corrupt, or usurp the decision- making of adversaries and potential adversaries while protecting our own (JP 3-13). Information operations (IO) integrate and synchronize information-related capabilities to create effects in and through the information environment and deliver an operational advantage to the commander. IO optimize the information element of combat power and support and enhance all other elements to gain operational advantage over a threat. IO consist of three inter-related efforts that work in tandem and overlap each other. These three efforts are—

- A commander-led staff planning and synchronization effort.
- A preparation and execution effort carried out by information-related capabilities units, IO units, or staff entities in concert with the IO working group.
- An assessment effort that is carried out by all involved.

2-77. When commanders employ cyberspace and EW capabilities to create desirable conditions within the OE, they synchronize these actions through IO. Commanders use cyberspace operations and EW to gain a strategic advantage in cyberspace and the EMS. Cyberspace and EW capabilities support operations by enabling the ability to share information among friendly forces or affecting the enemy's ability to use cyberspace and the EMS.

2-78. Cyberspace operations and EW effects influence, disrupt, corrupt, or manipulate the decision-making cycle of threat actors. Cyberspace operations support operations through OCO or DCO-RA by creating denial or manipulation effects to degrade, disrupt, or destroy the enemy's cyberspace capability or change enemy information, information systems, or networks. EW supports operations through EA by degrading, neutralizing, or destroying enemy capability to use the EMS. EW also supports operations through EP actions by concealing or manipulating friendly EMS signatures, to degrade or deceive enemy sensors or targeting systems. When integrated and synchronized with other capabilities, cyberspace operations and EW can help commanders set favorable conditions for information advantage, whether in cyberspace, the EMS, or other domains.

2-79. Cyberspace operations and EW can also create cognitive effects by impacting physical components of enemy capabilities. For example, affecting the ability of an enemy's fires network through a cyberspace attack or EA may deny or create doubt about their ability to use artillery effectively. Similarly, restricting the enemy's ability to use cyberspace or EMS at critical points can affect enemy judgments when exercising command and control. Synchronizing defensive EW and cyberspace operations with other capabilities can also disrupt a threat's ability to make decisions while ensuring friendly forces freedom of action.

2-80. Cyberspace operations and EW synchronized through the operations process and targeting can provide commanders additional ways and means to—

- Affect threat capabilities that inform or influence decision making.
- Affect threat capabilities for command and control, movement and maneuver, fires, intelligence, communications, and information warfare.
- Affect threat capabilities to target and attack friendly command and control and related decision support systems.
- Affect threat capabilities that distribute, publish, or broadcast information designed to persuade relevant actors to oppose friendly operations.
- Enable military deception directed against threat decision making, intelligence and information gathering, communications, dissemination, and command and control capabilities.
- Enable friendly OPSEC to protect critical information.
- Enable friendly influence activities, such as military information support operations, to improve or sustain positive relations with foreign actors in and around the operational area and to degrade threat influence over the same.
- Protect friendly information, technical networks, and decision-making capabilities from exploitation by enemy and adversary information warfare assets.

Other titles we publish on Amazon.com:

THIS IS MY ROBOT:
THERE ARE MANY LIKE IT,
BUT THIS ONE IS MINE

ATP 3-90.98
JUNGLE OPERATIONS

SEPTEMBER 2020
HEADQUARTERS, DEPARTMENT OF THE ARMY

STRYKER BRIGADE
COMBAT TEAM
WEAPONS TROOP

The Bear Went
Over the Mountain
Soviet Combat Tactics In Afghanistan

Chapter 3

Army Organizations and Command and Control

This chapter describes the cyberspace and electromagnetic warfare support available to Army maneuver commanders. It describes the roles, responsibilities, and capabilities of the United States Army Cyber Command and its subordinate organizations. This chapter details the cyberspace electromagnetic activities section and its roles and responsibilities. This chapter discusses interactions between the cyberspace electromagnetic activities section and other staff sections, including the role of the cyberspace electromagnetic activities working group.

SECTION I – ARMY CYBERSPACE OPERATIONS ORGANIZATIONAL STRUCTURE

3-1.   Army maneuver commanders use cyberspace operations and EW to understand the OE, support decision-making, and affect adversaries. Maneuver commanders at the brigade combat team level and above rely on assigned CEMA sections to leverage Army and joint cyberspace and EW capabilities. During joint operations, a corps or division designated as a JTF headquarters or a joint force headquarters combines its spectrum management chief with its CEMA section to establish an electromagnetic spectrum operations (EMSO) cell to support the joint electromagnetic spectrum operations cell (JEMSOC). Numerous Army and joint organizations contribute forces and capabilities for use in cyberspace operations and EW. Commanders at corps and below should possess a general understanding of the roles and responsibilities of these organizations and how they interact with the units' CEMA sections.

3-2.   This section provides an overview of Army organizations that provide cyberspace operations and EW support to Army commanders. It describes the Army's Service component command for cyberspace operations, United States Army Cyber Command (ARCYBER) and its subordinate elements.

UNITED STATES ARMY CYBER COMMAND

3-3.   ARCYBER operates and defends Army networks and delivers cyberspace effects against adversaries to defend the nation. ARCYBER rapidly develops and deploys cyberspace capabilities to equip our force for the future fight against a resilient, adaptive adversary. ARCYBER also integrates intelligence, fires, space, psychological operations, strategic communications, public affairs, special technical operations, cyberspace operations, electromagnetic warfare, and information operations to allow Army commanders a decisional advantage during competition and conflict.

3-4.   ARCYBER protects DODIN-A through DCO-IDM and DODIN operations. Commander, ARCYBER, is also the commander of joint force headquarters-cyber (JFHQ-C [Army]). In this role, Commander, ARCYBER, possesses the capability to conduct OCO to attack and exploit the enemy upon authorization from Unites States Cyber Command (USCYBERCOM). ARCYBER is the Army's point of contact for reporting and assessing cyber incidents and events involving suspected adversary activity. The United States Army Network Enterprise Technology Command (NETCOM) and the regional cyber center act as the chief action arms, having been delegated operational control and directive authority for cyberspace operations by ARCYBER for DODIN operations over all Army networks. ARCYBER serves as the Army's principal cybersecurity service provider and provides program oversight while NETCOM and the regional cyber centers act as the principal executors of the program. Units assigned to ARCYBER are—

- NETCOM.
- 1st Information Operations Command (Land).

- 780th Military Intelligence Brigade.
- Cyber protection brigade.
- 915th Cyber Warfare Battalion.

ARMY INFORMATION WARFARE OPERATIONS CENTER

3-5.   The Army Information Warfare Operations Center serves as ARCYBER's hub for coordinating, integrating, synchronizing, and tracking cyberspace operations, electromagnetic warfare (EW), IO, and answering intelligence requirements in support of national, regional, and Army directives. The Army Information Warfare Operations Center maintains global and regional situational awareness and understanding while executing mission command of all assigned or allocated Army cyber and IO forces.

3-6.   The Army Information Warfare Operations Center is composed of personnel with information-related capabilities expertise (IO, cyber, EW, psychological operations [forces], public affairs, civil affairs, military deception, United States Space Command and special technical operations), to include representatives from all staff functions and embeds from partner organizations. The Army Information Warfare Operations Center is responsible for integrating information-related capabilities across the staff into the command's current operations and plans processes. Additionally, the Army Information Warfare Operations Center —

- Receives reports from subordinate commands.
- Prepares reports required by higher headquarters.
- Processes requests for support (RFS).
- Publishes operation orders (OPORDs) and cyber tasking orders (CTOs).
- Consolidates Commander's critical information requirements.
- Answers requests for information from higher HQs, CCMDs, other Services and agencies.
- Assesses the overall progress of ongoing operations.

UNITED STATES ARMY NETWORK ENTERPRISE TECHNOLOGY COMMAND

3-7.   NETCOM leads global operations for the Army's managed portion of the DODIN, ensuring freedom of action in cyberspace, while denying the same to our adversaries. NETCOM secures, configures, operates, extends, maintains and sustains the DODIN-A. NETCOM supports DCO-IDM maneuver, creating and preserving its confidentiality, availability, and integrity. NETCOM's core mission encompasses all aspects of unclassified and classified network transporting, sharing, and storing. NETCOM's Army DODIN Operations Center executes command and control, oversees operational synchronization, provides continuous, real-time monitoring and reporting of global DODIN operations to ensure timely delivery of DODIN operational effects to Service and joint force commanders, and provides problem identification and resolution across the global network.

3-8.   Regional cyber centers continuously conduct DODIN Operations and enables DCO-IDM on the DODIN-A, ensuring Army and joint forces' freedom of action in cyberspace, while denying the same to adversaries. The regional cyber centers are globally postured in the continental United States, Europe, Korea, Pacific, and Southwest Asia to provide continuous, uninterrupted service in each theater of operations. Regional cyber centers are the point of contact for Army forces to report cyber incidents. Regional cyber centers exercise overall responsibility for protecting the DODIN-A.

UNITED STATES ARMY CYBER PROTECTION BRIGADE

3-9.   The cyber protection brigade defends key terrain in cyberspace to deter threats and deliver effects that ensure freedom of action for friendly forces while denying the same to our adversaries. The cyber protection brigade organizes, trains, equips, directs, and deploys cyber protection teams that serve worldwide to augment supported organizations organic network defenders for operations and exercises, as well as provide unit cyber defensive readiness assessments and assistance. The cyber protection brigade commander is authorized by standing order to conduct DCO-IDM missions, including cyberspace defense actions, to reconfirm and reestablish the security of degraded, compromised, or otherwise threatened blue cyberspace.

915TH CYBER WARFARE BATTALION

3-10.   The 915th Cyber Warfare Battalion is the Army's scalable expeditionary battalion composed of expeditionary CEMA team(s) (ECT). ECTs include cyberspace forces, EW CEMA operators, IO officers, a targeting cell, and intelligence personnel. The 915th Cyber Warfare Battalion's intelligence personnel collects information to support internal CEMA, and conducts intelligence analysis to support and ECT CEMA operations. ARCYBER deploys ECTs to provide cyberspace OCO, DCO, IO, and EW support for Army commands. ECTs have the capabilities to employ OCO, DCO, EW, and IO in support of Army operations. Certain CEMA operations require authorization and authorities delegated from USCYBERCOM, geographic combatant commanders, or commanders with electronic warfare control authority. The 915th Cyber Warfare Battalion is an Army only, Service-retained unit and not part of the DOD cyber mission force; however, all OCO missions conducted by the 915th Cyber Warfare Battalion must first be validated and authorized by USCYBERCOM.

1ST INFORMATION OPERATIONS COMMAND

3-11.   The 1st Information Operations (IO) Command is the Army's only Active Component Information Operations organization. It is a multi-component, brigade-level organization and it consists of a headquarters and headquarters detachment and two battalions. 1st IO Command's mission is to provide information operations and cyberspace operations support to the Army and other Services through deployable teams, reach back planning and analysis, and specialized training.

780TH MILITARY INTELLIGENCE BRIGADE-CYBER

3-12.   The 780th Military Intelligence Brigade (Cyber) conducts cyberspace operations to deliver effects in support of Army and joint requirements. The 780th Military Intelligence Brigade's primary objective is to enable and execute cyberspace operations. Elements of the brigade use SIGINT operational tasking authority delegated through Commander, ARCYBER, open source intelligence authority delegated through Commander, United States Army Intelligence and Security Command, and multiple cyberspace collection authorities delegated through Commander, USCYBERCOM to conduct reconnaissance and Intelligence to enable cyberspace operations. The headquarters serves as a force provider for ARCYBER and cyber national mission force (CNMF).

SECTION II – ELECTROMAGNETIC WARFARE ORGANIZATIONS

3-13.   This section outlines the joint and Army organizations available to corps and below units during joint and Army operations. It outlines and describes electromagnetic warfare platoons assigned to Army BCTs. It also provides an overview of the Intelligence, Information, Cyber, EW, and Space (I2CEWS) detachment assigned to a multi-domain task force.

ELECTROMAGNETIC WARFARE PLATOON (BRIGADE COMBAT TEAM)

3-14.   EW platoons are located in the military intelligence company of a brigade combat team's brigade engineer battalion. An EW platoon consists of three EW teams with the capability to provide EW support during close operations. Though the CEMA section aligns EW and cyberspace operations with the operations process, they must collaborate with the BCT's S-2 to task the military intelligence company for deploying EW platoon assets in support of assigned EW missions.

3-15.   The EW platoon performs electromagnetic reconnaissance to identify and locate enemy emitters and spectrum-dependent devices within assigned AO using sensors. Data and information attained through electromagnetic reconnaissance provide the commander with critical combat information. This data and information also supports electromagnetic battle management by providing continuous situational awareness to the CEMA spectrum manager to develop and update the common operational picture of the EMOE. An EW platoon can also conduct EA to degrade and neutralize enemy spectrum-dependent devices.

3-16.   When given electromagnetic attack control authority from the JTF headquarters, the JFLCC may further delegate electromagnetic attack control authority to subordinate Army commanders. Electromagnetic attack control authority is a broader evolution of jamming control authority that enables subordinate commanders with the authority to transmit or cease transmission of electromagnetic energy. Electromagnetic attack control authority allows commanders to control EA missions conducted throughout their AO within the constraints of their higher headquarters. Before receiving electromagnetic spectrum coordinating authority, commanders should ensure they have situational awareness of the EMOE, operational control of EW capabilities, and the ability to monitor and estimate EW transmission activities within their AO to determine corrective actions when necessary. Commanders should also ensure that EW missions are thoroughly vetted to ensure deconfliction with friendly spectrum dependent devices. The G-6 spectrum management chief or the G-6 or S-6 spectrum manager is responsible for performing electromagnetic battle management for the unit.

3-17.   EW platoons reprogram all assigned EW equipment according to system impact messages received from Service equipment support channels that include recommendations to respond to identified threat changes. Commanders may require an EW platoon to make immediate changes to their tactics to regain or improve EW equipment performance (See Appendix F for more information on EW reprogramming).

INTELLIGENCE, INFORMATION, CYBER, ELECTROMAGNETIC WARFARE, AND SPACE DETACHMENT

3-18.   The I2CEWS detachment is a battalion-sized unit assigned to a multi-domain task force and includes an enhanced CEMA section. The I2CEWS provides cyberspace operations and EW support to an Army Service Component Command, theater army, or the JTF conducting long-range precision joint strikes during multi-domain operations. The I2CEWS is composed of four companies consisting of cyberspace forces with the capability to perform Service-level DCO-IDM and EW operators capable of delivering EA effects throughout the MDTFs assigned AO.

3-19.   The I2CEWS has organic sensing and intelligence, information, and space operations assets that, when integrated and synchronized with DCO-IDM and EW, allows Army forces to simultaneously defend their assigned portion of the DODIN-A while disrupting, denying, and degrading enemy EMS capabilities. The I2CEWS is structured to meet the continually changing OE in which joint operations are being conducted collaboratively and simultaneously in multiple domains.

SECTION III – CYBERSPACE ELECTROMAGNETIC ACTIVITIES AT CORPS AND BELOW

3-20.   CEMA sections are assigned to the G-3 or S-3 within corps, divisions, BCTs, and combat aviation brigades. Commanders are responsible for ensuring that CEMA sections integrate cyberspace operations and EW into their concept of operations. The CEMA section involves key staff members in the CEMA working group to assist in planning, development, integration, and synchronization of cyberspace operations and EW.

> *Note.* The structure of the CEMA section is similar at all corps and below echelons. However, 1st IO Command may augment a corps' CEMA section to provide increased capabilities for synchronizing and integrating cyberspace operations and EW with IO (see Chapter 4).

COMMANDER'S ROLE

3-21.   Commanders direct the continuous integration of cyberspace operations and EW within the operations process, whether in a tactical environment or at home station. By leveraging cyberspace operations and EW as part of combined arms approach, commanders can sense, understand, decide, act, and assess faster than the adversary assesses and achieve a decisional advantage in multiple domains during operations.

3-22. Commanders should—
- Include cyberspace operations and EW within the operations process.
- Continually enforce cybersecurity standards and configuration management.
- Understand, anticipate, and account for cyberspace and EW effects, capabilities, constraints, and limitations, including second and third order effects.
- Understand the legal and operational authorities to affect threat portions of cyberspace or EMS.
- Understand the implications of cyberspace operations and EW operations on the mission and scheme of maneuver.
- Understand how the selected course of action (COA) affects the prioritization of resources to their portion of the DODIN-A.
- Leverage effects in and through cyberspace and the EMS to support the concept of operations.
- Develop and provide intent and guidance for actions and effects inside and outside of the DODIN-A.
- Identify critical missions or tasks in phases to enable identification of key terrain in cyberspace.
- Ensure active collaboration across the staff, subordinate units, higher headquarters, and unified action partners that enable a shared understanding of cyberspace and the EMS.
- Approve high-priority target lists, target nominations, collection priorities, and risk mitigation measures.
- Ensure the synchronization of cyberspace operations and EW with other lethal and nonlethal fires to support the concept of operations.
- Oversee the development of cyberspace operations and EW-related home-station training.

CYBERSPACE ELECTROMAGNETIC ACTIVITIES SECTION

3-23. The CEMA section plans, coordinates, and integrates OCO, DCO and EW in support of the commander's intent. The CEMA section collaborates with numerous staff sections to ensure unity of effort in meeting the commander's total operational objectives such as collaborating with the G-2 or S-2 to attain situation awareness and understanding of friendly, enemy, and neutral actors operating within the AO. The CEMA section is responsible for providing regular updates to the commander and staff on OCO and other supported operations conducted in the AO. The CEMA section is responsible for synchronizing and integrating cyberspace operations and EW with the operations process and through other integrating processes. Personnel assigned to the CEMA section are the—
- CEWO.
- Cyber warfare officer.
- EW technician.
- EW sergeant major (corps) or EW NCOIC (division).
- EW noncommissioned officer (NCO).
- CEMA spectrum manager.

CYBER ELECTROMAGNETIC WARFARE OFFICER

3-24. The CEWO is the commander's designated staff officer responsible for integrating, coordinating, and synchronizing actions in cyberspace and the EMS. The CEWO is responsible for understanding all applicable classified and unclassified cyberspace and spectrum-related policies to assist the commander with planning, coordinating, and synchronizing cyberspace operations, EW, and CEMA. A commander that has been delegated electromagnetic attack control authority from higher headquarters may further delegate it to the CEWO. Refer to ATP 3-12.3 for specific roles and responsibilities of the CEWO. Tasks for which the CEWO is responsible include—
- Advising the commander on effects in cyberspace (including associated rules of engagement, impacts, and constraints) in coordination with the staff judge advocate.
- Advising the commander of mission risks presented by possible cyberspace and EW vulnerabilities and adversary capabilities.

- Analyzing the OE to understand how it will impact operations within cyberspace and the EMS.
- Developing and maintaining the consolidated cyberspace and EW target synchronization matrix and recommending targets for placement on the units' target synchronization matrix.
- Assisting the G-2 or S-2 with the development and management of the electromagnetic order of battle.
- Serving as the electromagnetic attack control authority for EW missions when directed by the commander.
- Advising the commander on how cyberspace and EW effects can impact the OE.
- Receiving and integrating cyberspace and EW forces and associated capabilities into operations.
- Coordinating with higher headquarters for OCO and EW support on approved targets.
- Recommending cyberspace operations and EW-related CCIRs.
- Preparing and processing all requests for cyberspace and EW support.
- Overseeing the development and implementation of cyberspace operations and EW-related home-station training.
- Providing employment guidance and direction for organic and attached cyberspace operations and EW assets.
- Tasking authority for all assigned EW assets.

CYBER WARFARE OFFICER (CORPS AND BRIGADE) OR CYBER-OPERATIONS OFFICER (DIVISION)

3-25. The cyber warfare officer (corps and brigade) or cyber operations officer (division) assists the CEWO with integrating and synchronizing cyberspace operations into the operations process and provides insight into cyberspace capabilities. The cyber warfare officer or cyber operations officer collaborates with the CEWO in vetting and processing potential targets received from subordinate units for OCO effects. The cyber warfare officer or cyber operations officer—

- Assists the CEWO in the integration, coordination, and synchronization of cyberspace operations and EW with operations.
- Provides the CEWO with information on the effects of cyberspace operations, including associated rules of engagement, impacts, and constraints used to advise the commander.
- Assists the CEWO with developing and maintaining a consolidated cyberspace target synchronization matrix and assists in nominating OCO-related targets for approval by the commander.
- Assists the CEWO in monitoring and assessing measures of performance and effectiveness while maintaining updates on cyberspace operation's effects on the OE.
- Assists the CEWO in requesting and coordinating for OCO support while integrating received cyber mission forces into operations.
- Coordinates with unified action partners for cyberspace capabilities that complement or increase the unit's cyberspace operations posture.
- Coordinates cyberspace operations with the G-2 or S-2 and the G-6 or S-6.
- Develops and implements cyberspace operations-related home station training.

ELECTROMAGNETIC WARFARE TECHNICIAN

3-26. The Electromagnetic Warfare Technician (EWT) is a critical asset to the CEMA section and the EW platoon as they serve as the resident technical and tactical expert across all echelons. The EWT assist in the accomplishment of mission objectives by coordinating, integrating, and synchronizing CEMA effects to exploit and gain an advantage over adversaries and enemies in both cyberspace and the electromagnetic spectrum (EMS), while simultaneously denying and degrading adversary and enemy use of the same. Refer to ATP 3-12.3 for specific roles and responsibilities of the EW Technician. EWT duties include—

- Serves as the acting CEWO or EW platoon leader, when assigned position is vacant during assignment.

- Serves as the validator for EW training within the organization.
- Maintains and assists in developing the CEMA staff running estimate.
- Assists in development and management of enemy electromagnetic order of battle. Integrates threat electronic technical data, identified in the electromagnetic order of battle, as part of the IPB process.
- Advises on technical and tactical employment of Joint and Army EW systems, and integrates EW into the targeting process.
- Assists the CEWO with recommended EW COAs assets that suit each EW unit's mission.
- Coordinates targeting information and synchronizing EA and ES activities with Intelligence personnel (G-2 or S-2).
- Assists spectrum manager (G-6 or S-6) with EP technical data to enhance emission control for the unit.
- Conducts, maintains, and updates an electromagnetic environment survey.
- Identifies the enemy and friendly EMS-related effects.
- Assists Force Protection officer in developing mitigation measures for UAS when EW capabilities are used.
- Assists in developing and promulgating standard operating procedures (SOPs) and battle drills throughout the organization.
- Advises and oversees the acquisition of EW assets, including non-program of record equipment.
- Oversees the maintenance of organic EW assets.
- Assists the CEWO in preparing and updating the EW appendix to the operations order.
- Assists in production and application of target selection standards for EW.
- Develops and executes EW policies and procedures for supported organizations.
- Plans, organizes, implements, monitors and evaluates operations and the threat environment, in support of the CEWO.
- Requests and conducts battle damage assessments resulting from EW effects.

ELECTROMAGNETIC WARFARE SERGEANT MAJOR (CORPS) OR NCOIC (DIVISION)

3-27. The EW sergeant major or NCOIC is the CEWO's senior enlisted advisor for EW. The EW sergeant major or NCOIC assists the CEWO and cyber warfare officer with integrating, coordinating, and cyberspace operations and EW with operations. The EW sergeant major or NCOIC provides input to the CEWO on EW actions and their associated effects in the AO. The EW sergeant major or NCOIC assists the EW technician in updating and managing the electromagnetic order of battle.

3-28. The EW sergeant major or NCOIC assists the CEWO and cyber-warfare officer in developing and updating the cyberspace target synchronization matrix, specifically those targets related to EW, and assists with nominating EA-related targets for the commander's approval. The EW sergeant major or NCOIC provides input to the CEWO regarding how EW effects can influence the EMOE. Refer to ATP 3-12.3 for specific roles and responsibilities of the EW sergeant major or NCOIC.

3-29. The EW sergeant major or NCOIC collaborates with the EW technician with developing and implementing EW-related home station training. EW training development is a core responsibility of an EW sergeant major. The EW sergeant major evaluates all aspects of EW training and certifies instructors within subordinate organizations. The EW sergeant major ensures EW training is developed appropriately, reflects current methodology, and supports Army mission requirements.

ELECTROMAGNETIC WARFARE NONCOMMISSIONED OFFICER

3-30. The EW NCO manages the availability and employment of EW assets assigned to the unit. The EW NCO is the organization's senior training developer for EW. The EW NCO collects and maintains data for electromagnetic energy surveys and operates and maintains EW tools. The EW NCO assists the CEMA spectrum manager with frequency deconfliction. The EW NCO coordinates with the G-2 or S-2 to develop and conduct integrated SIGINT and ES training for EW personnel. When the commander or CEWO has electromagnetic attack control authority, the EW NCO helps manage EW assets during operations. The EW NCO assists the EW sergeant major or NCOIC with implementing EW-related home station training.

CYBERSPACE ELECTROMAGNETIC ACTIVITIES SPECTRUM MANAGER

3-31. The CEMA spectrum manager assists the CEMA section in the planning, coordination, assessment, and implementation of EW through frequency management. The CEMA spectrum manager defines the EMOE for the CEMA section. The CEMA spectrum manager—

- Forwards all reports of EMI identified by EW operators to either the G-6 or S-6 spectrum management chief or spectrum manager. Uploads the reports to Joint Spectrum Interference Reporting Online.
- In collaboration with the G-6 or S-6 spectrum manager, ensures the frequency deconfliction of spectrum management operations with EW.
- Assists the EW technician in developing and managing the electromagnetic order of battle.
- Synchronizes frequencies used during EW and cyberspace operations to protect radio frequencies used by friendly forces in collaboration with the G-6 or S-6 spectrum manager.
- Reports EMI from EW systems to the G-6 or S-6 spectrum management chief or spectrum manager for mitigation.
- Determines if EW assets have spectrum supportability and provide frequency-engineering support.
- Maintains frequency charts, diagrams, and reports of EMI incidents identified during EW missions.
- Assists the CEWO in issuing guidance throughout the organization regarding deconfliction and resolution of EMI between EW systems and other friendly systems.

CYBERSPACE ELECTROMAGNETIC ACTIVITIES WORKING GROUP

3-32. The CEMA section leads the CEMA working group. The CEMA working group is not a formal working group that requires dedicated staff members from other sections. When needed, the CEWO uses a CEMA working group to assist in synchronizing and integrating cyberspace operations and EW into the concept of operations. The CEMA section normally collaborates with key stakeholders during staff meetings established as part of the unit's battle rhythm and throughout the operations process. Membership in the CEMA working group will vary based on mission requirements.

3-33. If scheduled, the CEMA working group must be integrated into the staff's battle rhythm. The CEMA working group is responsible for coordinating horizontally and vertically to support operations and assist the fires support element throughout the execution of an operation. Generally, the CEMA working group is comprised of staff representatives with equities in CEMA, and typically include—

- The G-2 or S-2.
- The G-6 or S-6.
- The IO officer or representative.
- The G-6 or S-6 spectrum manager.
- The fire support officer or a fires support element representative.
- The staff judge advocate.
- The Protection Officer.

STAFF AND SUPPORT AT CORPS AND BELOW

3-34. During the operations process and associated integrating processes, cyberspace operations and EW require collaborative and synchronized efforts with other key staff. The G-6 or S-6 oversees DODIN operations, and the G-6 or S-6 spectrum manager collaborates with the CEMA spectrum manager to synchronize spectrum management operations with EW. The G-2 or S-2 manages the integration and synchronization of the IPB process and information collection. The IO officer oversees the integration and synchronization of information-related capabilities for IO. The staff judge advocate advises the commander on the legality of operations.

ASSISTANT CHIEF OF STAFF, INTELLIGENCE

3-35. The G-2 or S-2 provides intelligence to support CEMA. The G-2 or S-2 facilitates understanding the enemy situation and other operational and mission variables. The G-2 or S-2 staff provides direct or indirect support to cyberspace operations and EW through information collection, enabling situational understanding, and supporting targeting and IO. The G-2 or S-2 further supports CEMA by—

- Assessing CEMA intelligence and plans while overseeing information collection and analysis to support the IPB, target development, enemy COA estimates, and situational awareness.
- Continually monitoring intelligence operations and coordinating intelligence with supporting higher, lateral, and subordinate echelons.
- Coordinating SIGINT.
- Coordinating for intelligence and local law enforcement support to enhance cyberspace security.
- Leading the IPB and developing IPB products.
- Overseeing the development and management of the electromagnetic order of battle.
- Providing all-source intelligence to CEMA.
- Coordinating with the G-3 or S-3 and fires support element to identify high-value target(s) from the high-payoff target list for each friendly COA.
- Coordinating with the intelligence community to validate threat-initiated cyberspace attack or EA activities in the OE.
- Requesting intelligence support and collaborating with the intelligence community and local law enforcement to gather intelligence related to threat cyberspace operations and EW in the OE.
- Providing information and intelligence on threat cyberspace and EW characteristics that facilitate situational understanding and supports decision making.
- Coordinating with Air Force Combat Weather Forecasters for information on the terrain and weather variables for situational awareness.
- Ensuring information collection plans and operations support CEMA target development, target update requirements, and combat assessment.
- Developing requests for information and collection for information requirements that exceed the unit's organic intelligence capabilities.
- Collecting, processing, storing, displaying, and disseminating cyberspace operations and EW relevant information throughout the operations process and through command and control systems.
- Consolidating all high-value target(s) on a high-payoff target list.
- Providing input for guarded frequencies from the intelligence community.
- Providing the CEMA section and G-6 or S-6 prioritized EMS usage requirements for intelligence operations.
- Participating as a member of the CEMA working group.
- Assisting the CEMA spectrum manager in mitigating EMI and resolving EMS deconfliction and assisting with determining the source of unacceptable EMI.

ASSISTANT CHIEF OF STAFF, SIGNAL

3-36. In collaboration with the joint force and unified action partners (as appropriate), the G-6 or S-6 staff directly or indirectly supports cyberspace operations by conducting DODIN operations. G-6 or S-6 is the primary staff representative responsible for spectrum management operations. The G-6 or S-6 staff supports CEMA by—

- Establishing the tactical portion of the DODIN-A, known as the tactical network, at theater army and below.

- Conducting DODIN operations activities, including cyberspace security, to meet the organization's communications requirements.
- Assisting in developing the cyberspace threat characteristics specific to enemy and adversary activities and related capabilities within friendly networks, and advising on cyberspace operations COAs.
- Conducting cyberspace security risk assessments based on enemy or adversary tactics, techniques, and procedures, identifying vulnerabilities to crucial infrastructure that may require protection measures that exceed the unit's capabilities and require DCO-IDM support.
- Participating in the CEMA working group.
- Providing a common operational picture of the DODIN for planning purposes and situational awareness.
- Providing subject matter expertise regarding wired and wireless networks.
- Ensuring security measures are configured, implemented, and monitored on the DODIN-A based on threat reports.
- Overseeing spectrum management operations.
- Implementing layered security by employing tools to provide layered cyberspace security and overseeing security training throughout the organization.
- Coordinating with the regional cyber center to ensure the unit understands and meets compliance of all cyberspace operations policies and procedures within the region.
- Requesting satellite and gateway access through the regional satellite communications support center.
- Coordinating with regional hub node to establish network connectivity and access services.

INFORMATION OPERATIONS OFFICER (CORPS AND DIVISION) OR REPRESENTATIVE (BRIGADE AND BELOW)

3-37. The IO officer or representative leads the unit's IO element. The IO officer or representative contributes to the IPB by identifying and evaluating threats targeted actors in the AO. The IO officer or representative understands the command relationship with information-related capabilities units and builds rapport accordingly. The IO officer or representative collaborates with those information-related capabilities units to determine ways to optimize the information-related capabilities' effects with other information-related capabilities through synchronization. The IO officer or representative leads the planning, synchronization, and employment of information-related capabilities not managed by a capability owner or proponent. The IO officer or representative coordinates with the CEMA section with integrating cyberspace operations and EW into IO. The IO officer or representative's responsibilities include—

- Leading the IO working group.
- Identifying the most effective information-related capabilities to achieve the commander's objectives.
- Synchronizing cyberspace operations and EW with other information-related capabilities to achieve the commander's objectives in the information environment.
- Assessing the risk-to-mission and risk-to-force associated with employing cyberspace operations, EW, and other information-related capabilities in collaboration with the CEMA section.
- Identifying information-related capabilities gaps not resolvable at the unit level.
- Coordinating with Army, other Services, or joint forces for information-related capabilities to augment the unit's shortfalls.
- Providing information, as required, in support of OPSEC at the unit level.
- Collaborating with the CEMA section to employ cyberspace manipulation and EA deception tasks in support of military deception.
- Assessing the effectiveness and making plan modifications to employed information-related capabilities.
- Developing products that describe all military and civilian communications infrastructures and connectivity links in the AO in coordination with the G-2 or S-2.

- Locating and describing all EMS systems and emitters in the EMOE in coordination with the G-2 or S-2, CEMA section, and other information-related capabilities owners.
- Identifying network vulnerabilities of friendly, neutral, and threat forces in coordination with the G-2 or S-2, CEMA section, and other information-related capabilities owners.
- Providing understanding of information-related conditions in the OE in coordination with the G-2 or S-2.
- Participating in the military decision-making process and developing IO-related IRs.
- Participating member of the CEMA working group.
- Integrating IO into the unit's targeting process.
- Integrating non-organic information-related capabilities into operations.
- Ensuring IO-related information is updated in the common operational picture.
- Collaborating with the fire support coordinator for lethal and non-lethal effects.

G-6 OR S-6 SPECTRUM MANAGER

3-38. The G-6 or S-6 spectrum manager coordinates EMS usage for various communications and electronic systems and resources. The G-6 or S-6 spectrum manager supports CEMA by—

- Coordinating spectrum resources for the organization.
- Coordinating for spectrum usage with higher headquarters, host nations, and international agencies as necessary.
- Coordinating frequency allocation, assignment, and usage.
- Coordinating spectrum resources for communications assets used for deception operations.
- Coordinating with the higher headquarters' spectrum manager to mitigate EMI identified in the unit's portion of EMOE.
- Seeking assistance from the higher the headquarters' spectrum managers for a resolution to unresolvable internal EMI.
- Participating in the CEMA working group.
- Assisting the CEMA spectrum manager with deconflicting friendly EMS requirements with planned EW, cyberspace operations, and information collection.
- Collaborating with the CEMA spectrum manager to ensure the integration and synchronization of spectrum management operations with EW.

FIRES SUPPORT ELEMENT

3-39. The fires support element plans, coordinates, integrates, synchronizes, and deconflicts current and future fire support to meet the commander's objectives. Fire support coordination may include collaboration with joint forces and unified action partners. The fires support element coordinates with the CEMA section to synchronize, plan, and execute cyberspace attacks and EA as part of the targeting process. The fires support element support CEMA by—

- Leading the targeting working group and participating in the targeting board chaired by the commander.
- Assisting the G-2 or S-2 with synchronizing the information collection plan with cyberspace operations, EW, and other fires.
- Synchronizing joint, interorganizational and multinational assets, fire support, and sensor management of counter-fire radar assets.
- Providing the commander and staff with the status of the unit's deployed radars, including the zones that each radar is surveilling.
- Integrating and synchronizing cyberspace operations and EW with other fires support.
- Collaborating with the CEMA section and the G-2 or S-2 in developing and managing the high-payoff target list, target selection standards, attack guidance matrix, and targeting synchronization matrix, all of which include cyberspace attack and EA-related targets.

- Planning, preparing, executing, and assessing all aspects of fire support, incorporating cyberspace and EW effects, and addressing them in rehearsals.
- Developing a scheme of fires with the commander and G-3 or S-3 that includes cyberspace operations and EW.
- Reviewing target nominations from the joint target list added to the unit's target nomination list that requires non-organic resources for target engagement.
- Recommending prioritization of high-value targets for inclusion on the high-payoff target list.
- Nominating the prioritized unit target nomination list to higher headquarters for integration into the joint targeting process.
- Providing input to the information collection plan.
- Collaborating with the G-2 or S-2 in recommending target area(s) of interest.
- Participating in the CEMA working group.
- Adding cyberspace attack and EA to the fires synchronization matrix.
- Providing information requirements as input for information collection.
- Synchronizing reconnaissance and surveillance assets through the targeting process to identify proposed targets to support the execution of HPTs.
- Collaborating with the CEMA section to develop movement plans for all spectrum-dependent devices as part of EP while ensuring the continual movement of the unit's radars to avoid enemy detection.

STAFF JUDGE ADVOCATE

3-40. The staff judge advocate is the field representative of the Judge Advocate General and the primary legal adviser to the commander. The staff judge advocate also advises the CEMA working group concerning operational law, and the legality of cyberspace operations and EW, particularly those cyberspace and EW tasks that may affect noncombatants. The staff judge advocate is the unit's subject matter expert on the law of war, rules of engagement, the protection of noncombatants, detainee operations, and fiscal and contract law, providing commanders and staff with essential input on plans, directives, and decisions related to lethal and nonlethal targeting. The staff judge advocate supports CEMA by—

- Ensuring cyberspace and EW comply with applicable policies and laws.
- Reviewing potential cyberspace operations and EW according to relevant legal frameworks and authorities granted at national and combatant command levels.
- Participating in the CEMA working group to provide legal advice on cyberspace operations and EW.
- Participating in the targeting working group to discuss and debate proposed targets, and in coordination with other members, ensuring targets are realistic and meaningful, and the method of attack on a target is lawful.

Chapter 4

Integration through the Operations Process

This chapter discusses how the cyberspace electromagnetic activities section integrates cyberspace operations and electromagnetic warfare through the operations process. It outlines the four activities of the operations process and how the working group contributes to each activity. This chapter details how the cyberspace electromagnetic activities section and members of the working group synchronize cyberspace operations and electromagnetic warfare with intelligence preparation of the battlefield, information collection, targeting, risk management, and knowledge management processes.

SECTION I – THE OPERATIONS PROCESS

4-1.   At corps and below, the planning, synchronization, and integration of cyberspace operations and EW are conducted by the CEMA section, in collaboration with key staff members that make up the CEMA working group. The CEMA section is an element of the G-3 or S-3 and works closely with members of the CEMA working group to ensure unity of effort to meet the commander's objectives. Integration and synchronization of cyberspace operations and EW—

- Unifies Army and joint forces' effort to engineer, manage, secure, and defend the DODIN.
- Ensures information collected in cyberspace and the EMS is routed to the appropriate staff to provide the commander and staff for situational awareness of the OE, targeting, and as potential intelligence.
- Ensures the efficient use of cyberspace operations and EW assets for information collection and targeting.
- Ensures appropriate coordination between Army, joint, unified action partners and host nations before employing cyberspace operations and EW.

4-2.   The *operations process* includes the major command and control activities performed during operations: planning, preparing, executing, and continuously assessing the operation (ADP 5-0). The operations process is the Army's framework for the organization and implementation of command and control. The CEMA working group enables the commander with the ability to understand cyberspace and the EMOE. With this understanding, the commander can better visualize and describe an operation's end state and operational approach; this in turn enables the commander to make and articulate decisions, direct, lead, and assess operations. The commander and staff at a corps or division must align the commander's concept of operations with adjacent corps and divisions, joint forces, and unified action partners when conducting large-scale combat operations to ensure unity of effort.

4-3.   Commanders, staff, and subordinate headquarters use the operations process to organize efforts, integrate the warfighting functions across multiple domains, and synchronize forces to accomplish missions. Army forces plan, prepare, execute, and assess cyberspace operations and EW in collaboration with joint forces and unified action partners as required. Army commanders and staffs will likely coordinate or interact with joint forces to facilitate cyberspace operations and EW. For this reason, commanders and staff should have an awareness of joint planning systems and processes that enable cyberspace operations and EW. Some of these systems and processes include—

- The Joint Planning Process (See JP 5-0).
- Adaptive Planning (See JP 5-0).
- Review and approval process for cyberspace operations (Refer to Appendixes A and C).

- Joint Electromagnetic Spectrum Operations Planning Process (See JP 3-85).

PLANNING

4-4.   *Planning* is the art and science of understanding a situation, envisioning a desired future, and laying out effective ways of bringing that future about (ADP 5-0). Commanders apply the art of command and the science of control to ensure cyberspace operations and EW support the concept of operations. Whether cyberspace operations and EW are planned and directed from higher headquarters or requested from tactical units, timely staff actions and commanders' involvement coupled with continued situational awareness of cyberspace and the EMS are critical for mission success.

4-5.   The Army design methodology and military decision-making process are two planning methods used by Army headquarters. Members of the CEMA working group must understand these two methods fully. See Appendix A for a detailed discussion on how CEMA integrates cyberspace operations and EW within Army design methodology and the military decision-making process.

4-6.   The Army design methodology consists of more adductive and systemic reasoning for complex, ill-formed problems. The military decision-making process consists of a more deductive and analytical approach to planning and commanders at corps and below are likely to employ military decision-making process more frequently than Army design methodology. Commanders, however, may use a different approach to planning or combine approaches. Regardless of the planning approach, commanders and staff must integrate cyberspace operations and EW throughout the planning activity. During planning, commanders and staff should seek to—

- **Understand situations and develop solutions to problems.** The commander and staff build an understanding of the cyberspace domain, information aspects of the OE, and the EMOE within the assigned AO. Commanders and staff develop a situational understanding of the impact cyberspace operations and EW effects can cause throughout multiple domains and develop solutions to resolve issues that might negatively affect neutral entities and friendly forces.
- **Task-organize the force and prioritize efforts.** The commander and staff task-organizes cyberspace and EW capabilities and implement priority of support efforts. A *priority of support* is a priority set by the commander to ensure a subordinate unit has support in accordance with its relative importance to accomplish the mission (ADP 5-0).
- **Direct, coordinate, and synchronize action.** The commander and staff use this planning function to direct, coordinate, and synchronize cyberspace operations, EW, and spectrum management operations with missions conducted through intelligence operations, IO operations, and the targeting process.
- **Anticipate events and adapt to changing circumstances.** The commander and staff anticipate potential attacks by threats in cyberspace and the EMS and adapts to the uncertain nature of operations by implementing active and passive countermeasures associated with cyberspace security and EP. The commander and staff use such tools as decision points, branches, and sequels to adapt to changing circumstances (See ADP 5-0).

4-7.   The IPB process begins and is synchronized with the operations process during planning and continues throughout the operations process. During the IPB process, the G-2 or S-2 supports cyberspace operations and EW by providing the commander and staff with analyzed intelligence on the operational and mission variables in an area of interest to determine conditions relevant to those operations. This information assists the commander and staff in understanding the OE, identifying opportunities for cyberspace operations and EW, and determining appropriate COAs.

4-8.   During planning, the fires support element uses the commander's intent and concept of operations to develop a fire support plan. The fire support plan is a plan that addresses each means of fire support available. It describes how Army indirect fires, joint fires, and target acquisition are integrated with a maneuver to facilitate operational success (refer to FM 3-09). The fires support coordinator or support officer collaborates with the CEWO to integrate cyberspace attacks and EA into the fire support plan.

4-9.   The final product of planning is an operation plan (OPLAN) or operation order (OPORD). The OPLAN is developed by the commander and staff well in advance of execution and becomes an OPORD once directed for implementation based on a specific time or event. The CEWO is responsible for completing Annex C, Appendix 12, and upon request, assists the G-6 or S-6 with Annex H, Appendixes 1 and 6 of the OPLAN or

OPORD. The CEWO is also responsible for making updates, changes, and modifications to Annex C, Appendix 12 and assisting in updating Annex H, Appendixes 1 and 6 as appropriate, for fragmentary order(s) (FRAGORDs) (See Appendix A for Army design methodology, military decision-making process , and CEMA products for orders).

PREPARATION

4-10.   *Preparation* consists of those activities performed by units and Soldiers to improve their ability to execute an operation (ADP 5.0). Preparation activities include initiating information collection, DODIN operations preparation, rehearsals, training, and inspections. Preparation requires the commander, staff, unit, and Soldiers' active engagement to ensure the force is ready to execute operations.

4-11.   Preparation activities typically begin during planning and continue into execution. At corps and below, subordinate units' that are task-organized to employ cyberspace operations and EW capabilities (identified in the OPLAN or OPORD) conduct preparation activities to improve the force's opportunity for success during operations. Commanders drive preparation activities through leading and assessing. Using the following preparation functions, commanders and staff can—

- **Improve situational understanding.** Commanders, staff, and subordinate units continue to refine knowledge of cyberspace and the EMOE within the assigned AO, including the improved insight on how the use of cyberspace and the EMS could affect operations across multiple domains.
- **Develop a shared understanding of the plan.** Commanders, staff, and tasked subordinate units develop a shared understanding of the plan (described in the OPLAN or OPORD) by conducting home-station training and combat training center(s). These training events provide the perfect opportunity for subordinate commanders, leaders, and Soldiers to execute the developed plan in a controlled environment and to identify issues in the developing plan that require modification.
- **Train and become proficient in critical tasks.** Through rehearsals and training, subordinate units gain and refine skills in those individual and collective tasks essential to the success of cyberspace operations and EW. Commanders also allocate training time for anticipated and unanticipated events and circumstances.
- **Integrate the force.** Commanders allocate preparation time to put the new task-organized force into effect. Integrating the force includes detaching units, moving cyberspace and EW assets, and receiving and integrating new units and Soldiers into the force. Task-organized forces require preparation time to learn the gaining unit's policies and standards and to understand their role in the overall plan. The gaining unit requires time to assess the task-organized forces' cyberspace and EW capabilities and limitations and integrate new capabilities.
- **Ensure the positioning of forces and resources.** Positioning and task organization occur concurrently. Commanders ensure cyberspace and EA assets consist of the right personnel and equipment using pre-operations checks while ensuring those assets are in the right place at the right time.

EXECUTION

4-12.   *Execution* is the act of putting a plan into action by applying combat power to accomplish the mission (ADP 5-0). The commander, staff, and subordinate commander's focus on translating decisions made during planning and preparing into actions. Commanders conduct OCO and EA to project combat power throughout cyberspace and the EMS, conduct DCO and EP to protect friendly forces and systems, and conduct reconnaissance through cyberspace and the EMS to gather combat information for continuing situational awareness.

4-13.   Commanders should understand that detailed planning provides a reasonable forecast of execution but must also be aware that situations may change rapidly in cyberspace and the EMOE. During execution, commanders take concerted action to seize, retain, and exploit operational initiative while accepting risk.

4-14.   *Operational initiative* is the setting or tempo and terms of action throughout an operation (ADP 3-0). By presenting the enemy with multiple cross-domain dilemmas, including cyberspace and the EMS, commanders force the enemy to react continuously, driving the enemy into positions of disadvantage.

Commanders can use cyberspace attacks and EA to force enemy commanders to abandon their preferred courses of action and make costly mistakes. Commanders retain the initiative by synchronizing cyberspace attacks and EA as fires combined with other elements of combat power to apply unrelenting pressure on the enemy using continuously changing combinations of combat power at a tempo an enemy cannot effectively counter.

4-15.   Commanders and staff continue to use information collection and electromagnetic reconnaissance assets to identify enemy attempts to regain the initiative. Information collected can be used to readjust targeting priorities and fire support plans, including cyberspace attacks and EA, to keep adversaries on the defensive.

4-16.   Once friendly forces seize the initiative, they immediately exploit it through continued operations to accelerate the enemy's defeat. *Defeat* is to render a force incapable of achieving its objective (ADP 3-0). Commanders can use cyberspace attacks and EA to disrupt enemy attempts to reconstitute forces and exacerbate enemy disorganization by targeting adversary command and control and sensing nodes.

ASSESSMENT

4-17.   *Assessment* is the determination of the progress toward accomplishing a task, creating an effect, or achieving an objective (JP 3-0). The commander and staff continuously assess cyberspace operations and EW to determine if they have resulted in the desired effect. Assessment activities support decision making by ascertaining the progress of the operation to develop and refine plans.

4-18.   Assessment both precedes and guides the other activities of the operations process, and there is no single way to conduct it. Commanders develop an effective assessment plan built around the unique challenges of the operations. A Commander develops an assessment plan by—
- Developing the assessment approach (planning).
- Developing the assessment plan (planning).
- Collecting information and intelligence (execution).
- Analyzing information and intelligence (execution).
- Communicating feedback and recommendations (execution).
- Adapting plans or operations (planning and execution).

Note. For more information on the operations process, see ADP 5-0.

SECTION II –INTEGRATING PROCESSES

4-19.   Commanders and staff integrate warfighting functions and synchronize the force to adapt to changing circumstances throughout the operations process. The CEMA section aligns cyberspace operations and EW with the operations process and its associated integrating processes to identify threats in cyberspace and the EMS, to target and attack enemy cyberspace and EMS enabled systems, and to support the warfighting functions. Figure 4-1 on page 4-5 illustrates the integration and synchronization of CEMA throughout the operations process using the various integrating processes.

4-20. The operations process is the principal essential activity conducted by a commander and staff. The commander and staff integrate and synchronize CEMA with five key integrating processes throughout the operations process (see figure 4-1). These integrating processes are—

- IPB.
- Information collection.
- Targeting.
- Risk management.
- Knowledge management.

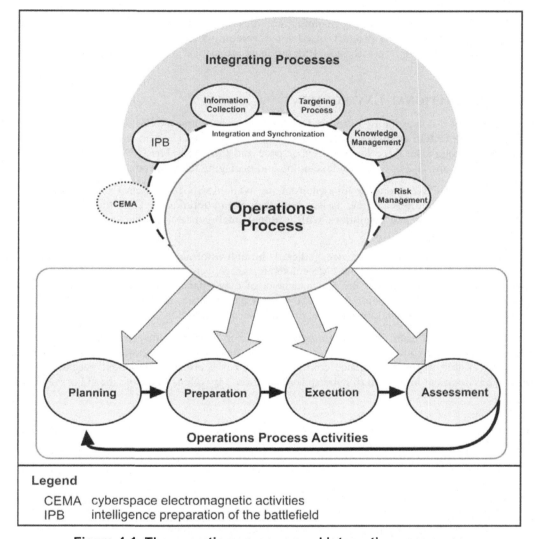

Figure 4-1. The operations process and integrating processes

INTELLIGENCE PREPARATION OF THE BATTLEFIELD

4-21.   To integrate and synchronize the tasks and missions of information collection, the G-2 or S-2 leads the staff through the IPB process. *Intelligence preparation of the battlefield* is the systematic process of analyzing the mission variables of enemy, terrain, weather, and civil considerations in an area of interest to determine their effect on operations (ATP 2-01.3). IPB assists in developing an in-depth understanding of relevant aspects of the OE, including threats.

4-22.   Integrating the IPB process into the operations process is essential in supporting the commander's ability to understand the OE and visualize operations throughout the operations process. Integrating the IPB process and the operations process is an enabler that allows commanders to design and conduct operations continuously. Integrating the IPB process and the operations process provides the information and intelligence required to plan, prepare, execute, and assess operations. Four steps in the IPB process are—

- Define the operational environment.
- Describe environment effects on operations.
- Evaluate the threat.
- Determine threat COAs.

4-23.   The IPB process begins during planning activities and continues throughout the operations process. The IPB process results in IPB products used for developing friendly COAs and decision points for the commander throughout planning activities. IPB products are critical to planning cyberspace operations and EW.

DEFINE THE OPERATIONAL ENVIRONMENT

4-24.   The G-2 or S-2 uses the IPB process to define cyberspace and the EMOE within an OE. Defining the cyberspace and the EMOE enables the commander and staff to visualize both friendly and enemy cyberspace and EW assets through the three layers of cyberspace and the EMS. The CEMA section supports the IPB process by assisting the G-2 or S-2 with developing and managing the electromagnetic order of battle.

4-25.   The G-2 or S-2 is responsible for synchronizing available SIGINT assets. Combat information attained through cyberspace operations and EW assists the G-2 or S-2 in defining the OE. Additionally, the G-2 or S-2 may combine the intelligence disciplines with criminal intelligence to gather cyberspace and EW-related information to define the OE fully.

4-26.   The G-2 or S-2 uses intelligence gathered through information collection to develop graphic AO overlays that include cyberspace and the EMS-related terrain aspects throughout the assigned AO. Graphic AO overlays of cyberspace may depict the physical layer of cyberspace more easily than the logical or cyber-persona layers. Attaining information on threat cyberspace capabilities at the logical and cyber-persona layers occurs through SIGINT, criminal intelligence, or cyberspace exploitation.

4-27.   The G3 should ensure information gathered by operational systems, platforms, and sensors, such as those used to monitor friendly networks during the execution of DODIN operations, is formally disseminated and made accessible to the intelligence community. This is a critical component necessary to define the operational environment in support of cyberspace operations, as well as to enable the G2 or S2 to evaluate the threat.

DESCRIBE ENVIRONMENTAL EFFECTS ON CYBERSPACE AND THE ELECTROMAGNETIC SPECTRUM

4-28.   As a result of answering IRs received from the CEMA section, the G-2 or S-2 defines the types of threats and threat cyberspace and EW capabilities while also defining environmental effects. It is essential to consider how environmental effects will impact friendly and enemy operations, including those that may affect cyberspace and the EMS. Such considerations include terrain, weather, light, illumination data, and civil. Terrain analysis allows the commander to understand the terrain's impact on cyberspace operations and EW. The CEMA working group conducts cyberspace and the EMS-related terrain analysis by employing traditional methods and examining the five military aspects of terrain when determining threat courses of action:

- Observation and fields of fire.
- Avenues of approach.
- Key terrain.
- Obstacles.
- Cover and concealment.

4-29.   Civil considerations are applied by cross walking with the operational variables. The G-2 or S-2 includes such civil considerations as cellular phone coverage, internet service providers, and electricity distribution for industrial, commercial, and residential areas.

4-30.   Threats in cyberspace and the EMS and all intelligence gathered and analyzed for environmental effects are incorporated into such IPB products as the threat overlays, threat description tables, terrain effects matrices, terrain analysis, or modified combined obstacle overlay, and assessments.

EVALUATE THE THREAT

4-31.   In collaboration with the CEMA section, the G-2 or S-2 determines threat cyberspace and EW capabilities, doctrinal principles, and tactics, techniques, and procedures used by the enemy in the assigned AO. An enemy's use of the cyberspace and the EMS to accomplish or support their objectives vary. Using input from the various intelligence disciplines, The G-2 or S-2 and CEMA section evaluate the threat, create threat models, develop broad threat COAs, and identify enemy high value targets (HVTs). When creating the threat model, the G-2 or S-2 incorporates cyberspace and EMS consideration to determine how the enemy integrates and uses cyberspace and EW capabilities.

4-32.   The enemy will likely have cyberspace and EW capabilities that operate across all warfighting functions. To increase situational awareness, the G-2 or S-2 should identify enemy cyberspace and EMS assets employed in support of each warfighting function. The G-2 or S-2 also evaluates neutral actors and adversaries conducting operations in cyberspace and the EMS throughout the AO and forwards the information to local and Army law enforcement or counterintelligence elements. Neutral actors and adversaries include—

● Nation-state actors.
● Transnational non-state actors or terrorists.
● Criminal organizations or multinational cyber syndicate actors.
● Individual actors, hacktivists, or small groups.
● Insider threats.
● Autonomous systems, software, and malicious code.

4-33.   Data gathered by evaluating the threat helps develop threat models that depict how enemy forces typically execute operations, including threat characteristics on how they use cyberspace and the EMS. The threat model also describes how enemy forces historically reacted to various types of cyberspace attacks and EA in similar circumstances relative to OE and overall operation.

4-34.   In addition to the threat model, the G-2 or S-2 creates threat capability statements that align with the threat model and include options or other supporting operations the enemy can use to affect the accomplishment of the friendly forces' mission. Threat models guide the development of threat COAs.

DETERMINE THREAT COURSES OF ACTION

4-35.   The G-2 or S-2 uses data gathered through threat evaluation to identify and develop the full range of COAs an enemy has available. The G-2 or S-2 collaborates with the CEMA section to develop threat COAs regarding an enemy's capabilities in cyberspace and the EMS. The G-2 or S-2 provides the G-3 or S-3 with information and intelligence necessary for developing friendly COAs to counter those available threats COAs and influence friendly operations. The G-2 or S-2 also collaborates with the CEMA section to develop countermeasures to threat COAs in cyberspace and the EMS. Each threat COA includes identified cyberspace attack and EA-related HVTs such as nodes, command and control centers, communications towers, satellites, internet service providers, fiber optic lines, and local power substations.

4-36.   When developing friendly COAs related to countering the enemy's capabilities in cyberspace and the EMS, the G-2 or S-2, in collaboration with the CEMA section, incorporates such considerations as the adversary's historical use of cyberspace and the EMS and the types of cyberspace and EMS-related operations they have conducted. The G-2 or S-2 assists the CEMA section in determining the unit's specific cyberspace and EW assets that can produce desired effects when engaging HVTs.

4-37.   The G-2 or S-2 should understand that a cyberspace threat could be operating outside of the unit's assigned AO. An enemy can use proxies worldwide beyond a unit's area of interest. Development of threat

COAs results from first identifying HVTs and HPTs. Threat COAs include templates and event matrices that identify potential objectives, named areas of interest and target areas of interest. A *named area of interest* is the geospatial area or systems node or link against which information that will satisfy a specific information requirement can be collected (JP 2-01.3). A *target area of interest* is the geographical area where high-value targets can be acquired and engaged by friendly forces (JP 2-01.3).

4-38.   The CEMA section conducts terrain analysis to examine aspects of terrain in cyberspace and the EMS for determining obstacles such as firewalls, port blocks, threat sensors, and jamming capabilities that require immediate mitigation for continued operation. The CEMA section also identifies the various avenues of approach to employ cyberspace attack and EA on enemy cyberspace and EMS capabilities. Through terrain analysis, the CEMA identifies potential weaknesses in friendly forces' posture in cyberspace and the EMS that require additional cover and concealment through such techniques as electromagnetic hardening actions, password protection, emission control, or by incorporating Internet Protocol (IP) hiding techniques.

4-39.   During terrain analysis, it is important to identify key locations in cyberspace and the EMS that can become access points. These access points provide avenues of approach or can provide observation and fields of fire where network traffic can be monitored, intercepted, or recorded through SIGINT, cyberspace exploitation, or ES. By identifying cyberspace and EW-related obstacles, avenues of approach, cover and concealment, and observation and fields of fire, the CEMA section can determine locations in those aspects of terrain to consider as key terrains. Key terrains include those major access points for observing incoming threats and avenues for launching cyberspace attack and EA. Terrain in cyberspace and the EMS connected to critical assets on the DODIN are considered as key terrains.

Note. For more information on the IPB process, see ATP 2-01.3.

INFORMATION COLLECTION

4-40.   *Information collection* is an activity that synchronizes and integrates the planning and employment of sensors and assets as well as the processing, exploitation, and dissemination systems in direct support of current and future operations (FM 3-55). These sensors and assets may include cyberspace operations and EW assets conducting cyberspace exploitation operations, electromagnetic probing, and electromagnetic reconnaissance for information collection.

4-41.   Information collection is the acquisition of information and the provision of this information to processing elements. Information collection integrates the intelligence and operations staff functions with a focus on answering the CCIRs, and IRs that assists the commander and staff in shaping the OE and conducting operations. The commander drives information collection coordinated by the staff and led by the G-2 or S-2. The following are the steps of information collection:
- Plan requirements and assess collection.
- Task and direct collection.
- Execute collection.

4-42.   Information collection enables the commander to understand and visualize the operation. Information collection identifies gaps in information that require aligning intelligence assets with cyberspace exploitation, electromagnetic reconnaissance, and electromagnetic probing to collect data on those gaps. The *decide* and *detect* steps of targeting also rely heavily on information collection. Enemy cyberspace capabilities identified through information collection assist the CEMA working group in identifying potential targets and key terrain in cyberspace.

PLAN REQUIREMENTS AND ASSESS COLLECTION

4-43.   The G-2 or S-2 collaborates with the other staff to receive and validate IRs for collection. The CEMA section provides the G-2 or S-2 with cyberspace and EMS-related IRs requesting information on friendly, enemy, and neutral actors operating in the AO. The CEWO identifies all cyberspace and EMS-related IRs to present to the commander as potential CCIRs. The G-2 or S-2 prepares the requirements planning tools and recommend cyberspace and EW assets for information collection to the G-3 or S-3.

TASK AND DIRECT COLLECTION

4-44.   In addition to the G-2 or S-2 using SIGINT for information collection, the G-3 or S-3 may task cyberspace and EW assets to support the information collection effort. In this instance, the CEMA section will assist the G-2 or S-2 by assigning organic EW assets while requesting additional EW and cyberspace assets as required. The G-2 or S-2 is responsible for maintaining the synchronization of all assets used for the information collection efforts.

EXECUTE COLLECTION

4-45.   The focus when executing information collection is to collect data that answers CCIRs and IRs for analysis during the IPB process. This information assists in shaping the OE and attaining information on the enemy. Collection activities acquire information about the enemy, including their cyberspace and EMS-dependent capabilities and assets. Collection activities begin shortly after the *receipt of the mission* activities of the operations process and continue throughout preparation and execution activities.

4-46.   The G-2 or S-2 executes collection by conducting—
- Intelligence operations.
- Reconnaissance.
- Surveillance.
- Security operations.

Intelligence Operations

4-47.   *Intelligence operations* are the tasks undertaken by military intelligence units through the intelligence disciplines to obtain information to satisfy validated requirements (ADP 2-0). Through intelligence operations, the G-2 or S-2 attains information regarding threat capabilities, activities, disposition, and characteristics. Intelligence operations use multiple intelligence disciplines to collect information regarding cyberspace and the EMS to satisfy CCIRs and IRs. However, knowledge attained from the other intelligence disciplines may also provide cyberspace and EMS related insight. In addition to gathering information on peer and near-peer threats through SIGINT, criminal intelligence collects information on cyberspace and EMS-related illegal activities conducted throughout the assigned AO. For more information on criminal intelligence, refer to AR 195-2.

Reconnaissance

4-48.   *Reconnaissance* is a mission undertaken to obtain, by visual observation or other detection methods, information about the activities and resources of an enemy or adversary, or to secure data concerning the meteorological, hydrographic, or geographic characteristics of a particular area (JP 2-0). Reconnaissance produces information about the assigned AO. Through reconnaissance, the G-2 or S-2 can collect information regarding such mission and operational variables as terrain characteristics, enemy and friendly obstacles to movement, and the disposition of enemy forces and civilians. Combined employment of three methods of reconnaissance (dismounted, mounted, and aerial) can result in the location and type(s) of friendly, civilian, and threat cyberspace and EW capabilities operating in the assigned AO. Upon request, the CEMA section supports the G-2 or S-2's reconnaissance efforts by employing EW assets to conduct electromagnetic reconnaissance to collect information in the EMS and request OCO support to conduct cyberspace exploitation in cyberspace.

Surveillance

4-49.   *Surveillance* is the systematic observation of aerospace, cyberspace, surface, or subsurface areas, places, persons, or things by visual, aural, electronic, photographic, or other means (JP 3-0). Surveillance involves observing an area to collect information and monitoring civilians and threats in a named area of interest or target area of interest. Surveillance may be autonomous or part of a reconnaissance mission. Collecting information in cyberspace and the EMS as part of a surveillance mission is also called network surveillance. *Network Surveillance* is the observation of organizational, social, communications, cyberspace, or infrastructure connections and relationships (FM 2-0). Network surveillance can also include detailed information on connections and relationships among individuals, groups, and organizations, and the role and importance of aspects of physical or virtual infrastructure.

4-50.   Information collected through network surveillance and other surveillance types are enablers to the IPB process. This collected information provides insight into enemy cyberspace and EW capabilities and assets. Upon request, the CEMA section supports the G-2 or S-2's surveillance efforts by requesting OCO support to employ cyberspace exploitation or by using EW assets to conduct electromagnetic reconnaissance to conduct surveillance in enemy and neutral cyberspace and the EMS. Information collected through cyberspace exploitation and electromagnetic reconnaissance includes mission and operational variables such as terrain characteristics, enemy and friendly obstacles, and the disposition of enemy forces and civilians.

Security Operations

4-51.   *Security operations* are those operations performed by commanders to provide early and accurate warning of enemy operations, to provide the forces being protected with time and maneuver space within which to react to the enemy and to develop the situation to allow commanders to effectively use their protected forces (ADP 3-90). Early and accurate warnings provide friendly forces with time and maneuverability to react and create an opportunity for the commander to employ force protection measures. Cyberspace defense, cyberspace security, and EP include actions that allow early detection and mitigation of threats in cyberspace and the EMS. Additionally, ES missions conduct electromagnetic reconnaissance to attain information about the disposition of enemy threats in the EMS and modify security efforts.

4-52.   The ultimate goal of security operations is to collect information on an enemy's COA that provide early warning and continuously disrupt enemy attacks. During security operations, information collected on an enemy's COA in cyberspace and the EMS allows units to take preemptive measures that prevent enemy intelligence, surveillance, and reconnaissance assets from determining friendly locations, strengths, and weaknesses. Security operations also present opportunities to identify HVTs for future cyberspace attacks or EA.

Note. For more intelligence information, see FM 2-0. For more details of information collection, see FM 3-55.

TERRAIN ASPECTS

4-53.   *Key terrain* is any locality, or area, the seizure or retention of which affords a marked advantage to either force (JP 2-01.3). Key terrain in cyberspace and the EMS is comparable to terrain in the other domains in that prevailing affords any combatant a position of advantage. Maintaining a secured prevalence in cyberspace and the EMS is a feasible objective when conducting cyberspace operations and EW. Seizing and retaining the entirety of cyberspace and the EMS to the exclusion of all enemies and adversaries is an unobtainable goal. It is also possible for both friendly and enemy forces to occupy the same terrain in cyberspace and the EMS or use the same processes for conducting operations in and through cyberspace and the EMS without knowing each other's presence. Another characteristic of terrain in cyberspace is that virtual components, identified in the logical network layer or the cyber-persona layer, constitutes locality in cyberspace. For this reason, identification of key cyberspace terrain is an essential component of planning cyberspace operations. Like the physical domain, commanders and staff must consider all of the military aspects of terrain. However, unlike the physical domain, commanders and staff must remember that the cyberspace terrain may change at any time. For example, an attacker may manipulate a firewall to create avenues of approach, or the enemy removing a node from the network may be a key terrain.

4-54.   Obstacles in cyberspace may include firewalls and port blocks. Avenues of approach in cyberspace can be analyzed to identify nodes and links that connect endpoints to specific sites. Cover and concealment may include hiding IP addresses or incorporating password-protected access to networks and network systems. Cyberspace observation and fields of fire include areas where network traffic can be monitored, intercepted, or recorded. Key cyber terrain provides access points to major lines of communications, key waypoints for observing incoming threats, launch points for cyberspace attacks and mission-relevant cyberspace terrain related to critical assets connected to the DODIN.

4-55.   Obstacles in the EMS may include electromagnetic environmental effects, enemy deployment of sensors and radars to detect friendly use of the EMS, and enemy employment of electromagnetic hardening, masking, and security measures. Avenues of approach in the EMS can be analyzed to identify spectrum-dependent systems, devices, and associated infrastructures that connect endpoints to specific locations (precision geolocation). Cover and concealment can include emission control or the implementation of such electromagnetic masking techniques as low-observability, low probability of intercept, and low probability of detection. EMS fields of fire include those areas in the EMS where enemy electromagnetic energy can be detected, identified, and evaluated through electromagnetic reconnaissance.

4-56.   Key terrain in the EMS includes frequencies used as access points and launch points to enemy spectrum-dependent systems, devices, and associated infrastructures. Key terrain also includes frequencies used for preemptive countermeasures, observing incoming threats, and critical assets dependent on the EMS. Key physical terrain is also imperative to the success of EW operations. Key terrain that provides superior line of sight over the adversary's position will help ensure friendly forces maintain a marked advantage over the adversary.

4-57.   Members of the CEMA working group need to match mission objectives with terrain analysis during planning to determine key terrain in friendly, neutral, and enemy cyberspace (See Appendix A). Correlating objectives with key terrain ensures mission dependencies in cyberspace and the EMS are identified and prioritized for protection. The results from interdependent systems, networks, and infrastructure that support a mission objective may require in-depth analysis to develop customized risk management.

TARGETING

4-58.   *Targeting* is the process of selecting and prioritizing targets and matching the appropriate response to them, considering operational requirements and capabilities (JP 3-0). A *target* is an entity or object that performs a function for the adversary considered for possible engagement or other actions. (JP 3-60).

4-59.   When targeting for cyberspace effects, the physical network layer is the medium through which all digital data travels. The physical network layer includes wired (land and undersea cable), and wireless (radio, radio-relay, cellular, satellite) transmission means. The physical network layer is a point of reference used during targeting to determine the geographic location of an enemy's cyberspace and EMS capabilities.

4-60.   When targeting, planners may know the logical location of some targets without knowing their physical location. The same is true when defending against threats in cyberspace. Defenders may know the logical point of origin for a threat without necessarily knowing the physical location of that threat. Engagement of logical network layer targets can only occur with a cyberspace capability.

4-61.   The logical network layer provides target planners with an alternate view of the target that is different from the physical network layer. A target's position in the logical layer is identified by its IP addresses. Targets located by their IP address depict how nodes in the physical layer correlate to form networks in cyberspace. Targeting in the logical layer requires the IP address and access to the logical network to deliver cyberspace effects. The ability of adversaries to change logical layer network configurations can complicate fires and effects against both logical and cyber-persona layer targets, but the operational benefit of affecting those targets often outweigh targeting challenges.

4-62.   The inability to target a cyber-persona in a distinct area or form in the physical and logical network layers presents unique complexities. Because of these complexities, target positioning at the cyber-persona layer often requires multiple intelligence collection methods and an extensive analysis to develop insight and situational understanding to identify actionable targets. Like the logical network layer, cyber-personas can change quickly compared to changes in the physical network layer.

4-63.   EA is exceptionally well suited to attack spectrum-dependent targets that are difficult to locate physically, cannot be accurately targeted for lethal fires, or require only temporary disruption. The fires support element plans, prepares, executes, and assesses fires supporting current and future operations by integrating coordinated lethal and nonlethal effects through the targeting process. Lethal and nonlethal effects include indirect fires, air and missile defense, joint fires, cyberspace attacks, and EA.

4-64.   Targeting is a multidiscipline effort that requires coordinated interaction among the commander, the fires support element, and several staff sections that form the targeting working group. The commander prioritizes fires to the targeting working group and provides clear and concise guidance on effects expected from all fires, including cyberspace attacks and EA. *Priority of fires* is the commander's guidance to the staff, subordinate commanders, fires planners, and supporting agencies to employ fires in accordance with the relative importance of the unit's mission (FM 3-09). The targeting working group determines which targets to engage and how, where, and when to engage them based on the targeting guidance and priorities of the commander.

4-65.   The targeting working group assigns lethal and nonlethal capabilities, including cyberspace attack and EA capabilities, to produce the desired effect on each target, ensuring compliance with the rules of engagement. The CEMA section participates in the targeting working group and provides recommendations for the employment of cyberspace and EMS-related actions against targets to meet the commander's intent and inclusion in the scheme of fires. *Scheme of fires* is the detailed, logical sequence of targets and fire support events to find and engage targets to accomplish the supported commander's objectives (JP 3-09).

4-66.   The CEMA section works closely with the fires support element to coordinate and manage cyberspace and EW assets as part of the fire support plan. This process is called fire support coordination and is the planning and executing of fire so that targets are adequately covered by a suitable weapon or group of weapons (JP 3-09).

TARGETING FUNCTIONS

4-67.   The G-2 or S-2, in collaboration with the CEMA section and the fires support element, detects, identifies, and locates targets through target acquisition. Effective employment of weapons, including EA and cyberspace attacks, require sufficient intelligence gained through target acquisition. The G-2 or S-2 conducts information collection to provide the fires support element, members of the targeting working group, and members of the targeting board with intelligence information used for targeting. This information includes threat cyberspace and EMS-enabled capabilities that require an individual or combined effect from lethal or nonlethal attacks.

4-68.   Targeting occurs continuously throughout operations. Army targeting methodology consists of four functions: decide, detect, deliver, and assess (D3A). These targeting functions occur throughout the operations process. Commanders and staff should also be conversant with joint targeting methodology and understand how each of these processes and methodologies relate, because cyberspace operations and EW are usually coordinated by a joint force commander. Table 4-1, page 4-13, illustrates a crosswalk between the operations process, the joint targeting cycle, D3A, and military decision-making process.

Table 4-1. Targeting crosswalk

Operations Process		Joint Targeting Cycle	D3A	Military Decision-Making process	Targeting Tasks
Continuous Assessment	Plan	1. Commander's Objectives, Targeting Guidance, and Intent.	Decide	Mission Analysis	• Perform target value analysis to develop fire support (including cyberspace, electromagnetic warfare, and information related capabilities) high-value targets. • Provide fire support, information-related capabilities, cyberspace, and electromagnetic warfare related input to the commander's targeting guidance and desired effects.
		2. Target Development and Prioritization.		Course of Action Development	• Designate potential high-payoff targets. • Deconflict and coordinate potential high-payoff targets. • Develop a high-payoff target list. • Establish target selection standards. • Develop an attack guidance matrix. • Develop fire support, cyberspace, and electromagnetic warfare related tasks. • Develop associated measures of performance and measures of effectiveness.
		3. Capabilities Analysis.		Course of Action Analysis	• Refine the high-payoff target list. • Refine the target selection standard. • Refine the attack guidance matrix. • Refine fire support tasks. • Refine associated measures of performance and measures of effectiveness.
		4. Commander's Decision and Force Assignment.		Orders Production	• Finalize the high-payoff target list. • Finalize target selection standards. • Finalize the attack guidance matrix. • Finalize the targeting synchronization matrix. • Finalize fire support tasks. • Finalize associated measures of performance and measures of effectiveness. • Submit information requirements to battalion or brigade G-2/S-2.
	Prepare	5. Mission Planning and Force Execution.	Detect		• Execute Information Collection Plan. • Update information requirements as they are answered. • Update the high-payoff target list, attack guidance matrix, and targeting synchronization matrix. • Update fire support, cyberspace, and electromagnetic warfare related tasks. • Update associated measures of performance and measures of effectiveness

Table 4-1. Targeting crosswalk (continued)

Operations Process		Joint Targeting Cycle	D3A	Military Decision-Making Process	Targeting Tasks
	Execute	6. Assessment	**Deliver**		• Execute fire support, cyberspace attacks, and electromagnetic attacks according to the attack guidance matrix and the targeting synchronization matrix.
	Assess		**Assess**		• Assess task accomplishment (as determined by measures of performance). • Assess effects (as determined by measures of effectiveness). • Refine fire support tasks and associated measures and reengage target if required

Legend:
D3A   decide, detect, deliver, and assess

Decide

4-69.   The decide function is the first step of the targeting process. It begins with the military decision-making process and continues throughout an operation. The CEMA section conducts the following actions during the decide function of targeting—

- Threat cyberspace and EW-related capabilities and characteristics during target value analysis to identify high-value targets. A *high-value target* is a target the enemy commander requires for the successful completion of the mission (JP 3-60).
- Identifying potential cyberspace and EW-related HPTs. A *high-payoff target* is a target whose loss to the enemy will significantly contribute to the success of the friendly course of action (JP 3-60). A high-payoff target is a high-value target that must be acquired and successfully engaged for the success of the commander's mission.
- Specific targets that should be acquired and engaged using a cyberspace attack or EA capability and established target selection standards.
- Location and time that targets are likely to be found through intelligence operations and how long the target will remain fixed.
- Surveillance, reconnaissance, and target acquisition objectives for targets receiving cyberspace attacks or EA and determining if the unit has the necessary cyberspace attack or EA capabilities to deliver appropriate effects.
- Cyberspace and EMS-related IRs essential to the targeting effort.
- When, where, and with what priority should the targets be engaged, and what cyberspace attack or EA capability to employ for effects.
- The level of effectiveness that constitutes a successful cyberspace attack or EA and if the engagement achieved the commander's objective.
- If a cyberspace attack or EA can affect a target, and how and what type of cyberspace attack or EA can create the desired effect.
- How to obtain the information needed to assess a cyberspace attack or EA to determine success or failure, and who will receive and process it.
- Who will be the decision-making authority to determine the success or failure of a cyberspace attack or EA?
- What contingency action will occur if a cyberspace attack or EA is unsuccessful, and who has the authority to direct those actions?
- Identifying the unit's EW assets available for tasking and begin drafting FRAGOS.
- Drafting the RFS for OCO support to meet targeting requirements.
- Collaborating with units at higher, lower, and adjacent echelons for EW support to satisfy identified gaps in EW capabilities.

- Drafting the Joint Tactical Air Request for airborne EA and other necessary EW requesting forms, if required.
- Open communications with the higher command to receive updates on whether anticipated cyberspace attack and EA-related targets have been validated and added to the JTF headquarters' joint target list.
- Discussing cyberspace and EW-related risk that the commander will use to make risk determinations.
- Determining the level of authorities for the engaging targets using cyberspace and electromagnetic attacks.

4-70. During the decide function, the targeting working group identifies target restrictions that prohibit or restrict cyberspace attacks or EA on specified targets without approval from higher authorities. The sources of these restrictions include military risk, the law of war, rules of engagement, or other considerations. The JTF annotates entities within the AO prohibited from attack on the no-strike list and targets with restrictions on the restricted target list.

Detect

4-71. The detect function of the targeting process is the second step of the targeting process; during this step ES capabilities or other target acquisition assets locate and track a specified target to the required level of accuracy in time and space. During the detect function, the G-2 or S-2 coordinates with the targeting working group in developing the information collection plan. Before conducting the deliver function, the targeting team must establish measures of performance and measures of effectiveness for cyberspace and electromagnetic attacks to ensure they meet the commander's objectives.

4-72. The targeting working group focuses on the surveillance effort by identifying named areas of interest and target areas of interest integrated into the information collection plan. Named areas of interest are typically selected to capture indications of adversary courses of action but may be related to conditions of the OE.

4-73. The targeting working group identifies HPTs during planning and war-gaming. Target areas of interest that require specific engagements using cyberspace attack or EA capabilities differ from engagement areas. An engagement area is an area of concentration where a commander employs all available weapons to engage a target. In contrast, a target area of interest engagement uses a specific weapons system to engage a target. During the detect function, the CEMA section conducts the following actions–

- Provides cyberspace and EW-related IRs to determine HPTs that, when validated by the commander, are added to the priority intelligence requirement.
- Tasks EW assets, when required, to conduct electromagnetic reconnaissance to support information collection.
- Updates cyberspace attack and EA-related HVTs and HPTs.
- Determines if identified targets can be affected using OCO or EA (or both), and what type of EA capability can create the desired effect

---

Note. The CEMA section alone cannot determine the type of cyberspace attack capability to use on targets. The CEMA section must coordinate with higher headquarters CEMA staff and appropriate joint cyberspace entities to develop an understanding of availability, feasibility, and suitability of specific cyberspace capabilities.

- Advocating for the nomination of cyberspace attack and EA-related targets to the JTF headquarters' joint integrated prioritized target list and the joint targeting cycle.
- Developing the RFS for OCO support.

Deliver

4-74. The deliver function of the targeting process executes the target engagement guidance and supports the commander's battle plan upon confirmation of the location and identity of HPTs. Close coordination between the CEMA section, intelligence, and fires support element is critical when detecting targets and delivering cyberspace attacks and EA. The fire support coordinator or fire support officer details fires coordination in the OPLAN or OPORD or target synchronization matrix.

Assess

4-75.   The assess function occurs throughout the operations process. During the assess function, targets are continuously refined and adjusted by the commander and staff in response to new or unforeseen situations presented during operations. Combat assessment measures the effectiveness of cyberspace attack and EA capabilities on the target and concludes with recommendations for reattack, continued attack, or to cease an attack. Recommendations for reattack, continued attack, and ceasing EA are combined G-3 or S-3 and intelligence functions approved by the commander. For more information on the targeting cycle and target development process, see ATP 3-60.

CONSIDERATIONS WHEN TARGETING

4-76.   The fires support element, in collaboration with the G-3 or S-3 and G-2 or S-2, uses targeting cycles and target development processes to select, prioritize, determine the type of effects, and duration of effects on targets. CEMA's planning, integrating, synchronizing, and assessing cyberspace operations and EW becomes apparent during the targeting process. Three important aspects of cyberspace and EW operations that require consideration during targeting processes are—

- Characteristics of cyberspace and electromagnetic warfare capabilities.
- Cascading, compounding, and collateral effects.
- Reversibility of effects.
- Considerations when requesting OCO support for targeting.

CHARACTERISTICS OF CYBERSPACE AND ELECTROMAGNETIC WARFARE CAPABILITIES

4-77.   Cyberspace capabilities are developed based on gathered intelligence and from operational and mission variables attained regarding an OE. In cyberspace operations, cyberspace forces consider such conditions as the type of computer operating system used by an enemy or adversary, the make and model of the hardware, the version of software installed on an enemy or adversary's computer, and the availability of cyberspace attack resources before creating effects on a target.

4-78.   EW capabilities are also developed based on gathered intelligence on operational and mission variables attained regarding an EMOE. In EW, targeting planners compare the types and capabilities of known spectrum-dependent devices that enemies use to the availability of EW resources before creating EW effects on a target. Targets include enemy spectrum-dependent devices carried by personnel and spectrum dependent systems used with or in weapons systems, sensory systems, facilities, and cyberspace capabilities that require the use of the EMS.

CASCADING, COMPOUNDING, AND COLLATERAL EFFECTS

4-79.   The CEMA section should understand the overlaps amongst the military, other government, corporations, and private sectors in cyberspace. These overlaps are particularly important for estimates of possible cascading, compounding, or collateral effects when targeting enemy and adversary cyberspace capabilities. The same level of consideration is required when targeting enemy and adversary spectrum-dependent devices in the EMS.

4-80.   Cyberspace capabilities can create effects beyond the geographic boundaries of an AO and a commander's area of interest. Employing cyberspace capabilities for attack or manipulation purposes within an area of interest require additional authorities beyond those given to a corps and below commander. Effects resulting from cyberspace attack operations can cause cascading effects beyond the targeted system that were not evident to the targeting planners. Cascading effects can sometimes travel through subordinate systems to attain access to the targeted system. Cascading effects can also travel through lateral or high-level systems to access a targeted system. Compounding effects are a gathering of various cyberspace effects that have interacted in ways that may have been either intended or unforeseen. Effects resulting from EA can cause cascading effects in the EMS beyond enemy or adversary's spectrum-dependent devices, disrupting or denying friendly forces access to the EMS throughout the EMOE.

4-81.   Collateral effects, including collateral damage, are the accidental cyberspace or EW effects of military operations on non-combatant and civilian cyberspace or EW capabilities that were not the intended target when implementing fires.

Note. Rules of Engagement or an operations order may limit cyberspace or EW operations to only those cyberspace or EW tasks that may result in no or minimal collateral effects. The CEMA spectrum manager must deconflict the joint restriction frequency list to mitigate EMI before all EW missions.

REVERSIBILITY OF EFFECTS

4-82.   Targeting planners must consider the level of control that they can exercise throughout each cyberspace and electromagnetic attack. Categorization of reversibility of effects are—

- **Operator reversible effects.** These effects can be recalled, recovered, or terminated by friendly forces. Operator reversible effects typically represent a lower risk of undesired consequences, including discovery or retaliation.
- **Non-operator reversible effects.** These are effects that targeting planners cannot recall, recover, or terminate after execution. Non-operator reversible effects typically represent a higher risk of response from the threat or other undesired consequences and may require more coordination.

Considerations When Requesting Offensive Cyberspace Operations for Targeting

4-83.   The integration of OCO into the targeting process requires both long-term preparation and real-time mission planning during execution activities of the operations process. Due to target development and access to both OCO capabilities and access to an enemy in cyberspace, it is essential to emphasize the necessity for long-term preparation and planning of OCO for deliberate targets and effects.

4-84.   When planning for OCO support to attack deliberate targets, the CEMA working group should consider the following:

- Determine if the target is targetable using OCO. Generally, the only potential targets that receive effects from a cyberspace attack are actively functioning in some portion of the information environment (data or information generation, processing, storage, communications, and digital data consumption or destruction).
- Ensure the target has not already been nominated or on an existing targeting list. If it has not already been nominated or placed on a current targeting list, it will require nomination for further target development.
- Consolidate all answered CCIRs and IRs. CCIRs and IRs may include such threat cyberspace intelligence as—links or nodes; associated hardware or software; specific software versions and configurations, communications protocol; physical or logical dependencies; or specific identifiers (IP address, machine access control address, international mobile subscriber identity, or phone numbers).
- Determine if intelligence attained through the IPB also includes information necessary to tailor targeting development on avenues to gain access to an enemy's cyberspace capabilities. Approaches to attain access to an enemy's cyberspace capabilities include—telephony, IP, embedded systems, and radio frequencies.
- The CEMA section is responsible for providing regular updates on a combat mission team's ability to conduct OCO as well as provide updated information on the supported operation.

Note. Access to an enemy's cyberspace capability does not guarantee the success of an employed cyberspace attack. The combat mission team must tailor the capability to create the desired effect on an enemy's cyberspace capability.

RISK MANAGEMENT

4-85.   *Risk management* is the process to identify, assess, and control risks and make decisions that balance risk cost with mission benefits (JP 3-0) and an element of command and control. Risk is the exposure of someone or something valued to danger, harm, or loss, and is inherent in all operations. The commander and staff conduct risk management throughout the operations process to identify and mitigate risks associated with hazards that can cause friendly and civilian casualties, damage or destruction of equipment, or otherwise impact mission effectiveness. Aspects of cyberspace defense and security operations and EP missions include risk mitigation measures as part of risk management.

4-86.   Risk management is integrated into planning activities and continues throughout the operations process. Risk management consists of the following steps:

- Identify the hazards.
- Assess the hazards.
- Develop controls and make risk decisions.
- Implement controls.
- Supervise and evaluate.

4-87.   The CEMA section, as with all staff elements, incorporate risk management into cyberspace operations and EW-related running estimates and recommendations to mitigate risk. The G-3/S-3 coordinates risk management amongst all staff elements during the operations process. For more information on the risk management process, see ATP 5-19.

RISKS IN CYBERSPACE AND THE ELECTROMAGNETIC SPECTRUM

4-88.   Risk is inherent in all military operations. When commanders accept risks, they create opportunities to seize, retain, and exploit the initiative and achieve decisive results. The willingness to incur risks is often the key to exposing an enemy's weaknesses that the enemy considers beyond friendly reach. Commanders assess and mitigate risks continuously throughout the operations process. Many risks to the DODIN-A come from enemies, adversaries, and insiders. Some threats are well equipped and well trained, while some are novices using readily available and relatively inexpensive equipment and software. Army users of the DODIN are trained on basic cyberspace security, focusing on the safe use of information technology and understanding common threats in cyberspace.

4-89.   Risk management is the Army's primary decision-making process for identifying hazards and controlling risks. The process applies to all types of operations, tasks, and activities, including cyberspace operations. The factors of mission, enemy, terrain and weather, troops and support available, time available, and civil considerations provide a standardized methodology for addressing both threat and hazard-based risks. Risks associated with cyberspace operations fall into four major categories—

- Operational risks.
- Technical risks.
- Policy risks.
- Operations security risks.

Operational Risks

4-90.   Operational risks pertain to the consequences that cyberspace and EMS threats pose to mission effectiveness. Operational consequences are the measure of cyberspace attack and EA effectiveness. Cyberspace intrusions or attacks, and likewise in the EMS, can compromise networks, systems, and data, which can result in operational consequences such as injury or death of personnel, damage to or loss of equipment or property, degradation of capabilities, mission degradation, or even mission failure. Exfiltration of data from

Army networks by the enemy can undermine the element of surprise and result in loss of initiative. Enemy or adversary forces may conduct cyberspace and EMS attacks to exposed friendly networks and capabilities, compromising future cyberspace attacks and cyberspace exploitation missions.

4-91.   Friendly forces conducting cyberspace operations and EW encounter many operational risks. Commander and staff consider cascading effects because of employing cyberspace attacks and EA. The CEMA section ensures that the commander and staff understand the characteristics of the various cyberspace and EW capabilities and their associated effects. The CEMA section informs the commander and staff of the reversibility of effects resulting from cyberspace attacks and EA to understand that some effects are irreversible at the operator level. Attaining an understanding of the characteristics, cascading effects, and reversibility effects provide a commander with situational awareness and in determining the acceptable risks when conducting cyberspace operations and EW.

4-92.   It is essential to consider risk management when conducting OCO and EA that could reveal friendly locations and intentions to an adversary prematurely. Some OCO or EA effects have a one-time use and once utilized cannot be effectively used again. OCO and EA may also create cascading effects that could hinder other operations.

4-93.   Personal electronic device(s) such as smartwatches, smartphones, tablets, laptops, and gaming systems can be a significant OPSEC vulnerability to friendly cyberspace and EW capabilities. The CEWO gathers understanding surrounding risks associated with PEDs from the G2 or S2 and OPSEC and makes recommendations to the commander regarding their usage in the organization.

Technical Risks

4-94.   Technical risks exist when there are exploitable vulnerabilities in systems on the DODIN-A, and there are threats that can exploit those vulnerabilities. Nearly every technical system within the Army is networked, resulting in a vulnerability in one system compromising other connected systems, creating a shared vulnerability. These potentially vulnerable networked systems and components directly impact the Army's ability to conduct operations. DCO mitigates risks by defending against specified cyberspace attacks, thereby denying the enemy's ability to take advantage of technical vulnerabilities that could disrupt operations.

4-95.   Robust information systems engineering disciplines result in chain risk management, security, counterintelligence, intelligence, and hardware and software assurance that assist the leaders with managing technical risk. Friendly forces examine the technical risks when conducting cyberspace attacks to avoid making friendly networks vulnerable to enemy cyberspace counterattacks. The Army uses a layering approach, using these elements—

- Antivirus and anti-malware programs.
- Employing firewalls.
- Updating firmware and patches.
- Employing network intrusion detection and monitoring sensors.
- Implementing both cybersecurity and physical security measures to mitigate technical risks.

4-96.   The elements listed in paragraph 4-95 are essential defensive enablers when implemented effectively and updated regularly.

Policy Risks

4-97.   Policy risk pertains to authorities, legal guidance, and international law. Policies address cyberspace boundaries, authorities, and responsibilities. Commanders and decision makers must perform risk assessments and consider known probable cascading and collateral effects due to overlapping interests between military, civil, government, private, and corporate activities on shared networks in cyberspace. Policies, the United States Code (USC), the Uniform Code of Military Justice, regulations, publications, operation orders, and standard operating procedures all constitute a body of governance for making decisions about activities in cyberspace.

4-98.   Policy risk includes considering international norms and practices, the effect of deviating from those norms, and potential shifts in international reputation because of the effects resulting from a cyberspace operation. Cyberspace attacks can be delivered through networks owned, operated, and geographically located within the sovereignty of multiple governments. EA can also deliver effects that impact frequencies in the spectrum owned and operated by commercial, government, and other neutral users. Therefore, it is vital to consider the legal, cultural, and political costs associated with using cyberspace and the EMS as avenues of approach.

4-99.   Policy risks occur where policy fails to address operational necessity. For example, a policy emplaced that limits cyberspace operations, which results in low levels of collateral effects, can result in a unit constrained to cyberspace attacks that will not result in the desired outcomes necessary for mission success. A collateral effects analysis to meet policy limits is distinct from the proportionality and necessity analysis required by the law of war. Even if a proposed cyberspace operation is permissible after a collateral effect's analysis, the proposed cyberspace operation or EW mission must include a legitimate military objective that is also permissible under the law of war.

4-100.   Policy risk applies to risk management under civil or legal considerations. An OCO or EA mission may pose a risk to host nation civilians and non-combatants in an OE where a standing objective is to minimize collateral damage. During a mission, it may be in the Army's best interest for host nation populations to be able to perform day-to-day activities. Interruptions of public networks may present hazards to the DODIN-A and pose dangers to Army forces because of social impacts that lead to riots, criminal activity, and the emergence of insurgent opportunists seeking to exploit civil unrest.

Operations Security Risks

4-101.   Both cyberspace and the EMS provides a venue for OPSEC risks. The Army depends on cyberspace security programs and training to prevent or mitigate OPSEC risks. Commanders emphasize and establish OPSEC programs to minimize the risks. OPSEC measures include actions and information on the DODIN and non-DODIN information systems and networks. All personnel are responsible for protecting sensitive and critical information. EP denies unauthorized access to information that an enemy intercept in the EMS through electromagnetic security operations. For more information on OPSEC, refer to AR 530-1 and ATP 3-13.3.

KNOWLEDGE MANAGEMENT

4-102.   *Knowledge management* is the process of enabling knowledge flow to enhance shared understanding, learning, and decision making (ADP 6-0). The four components of knowledge management are people, processes, tools, and organizations. Knowledge management facilitates the transfer of knowledge among the commander, staff, and forces to build and maintain situational awareness and enhance organizational performance. Through knowledge management, information gets to the right personnel at the right time to facilitate decision making.

4-103.   During knowledge management, the necessary cyberspace operations and EW-related information and tools from higher headquarters are provided to the CEMA working group in a timely enough manner to make decisions during mission analysis and COA development. Through the knowledge management process, cyberspace operations and EW-related intelligence received through information collection and IO is disseminated for decision making by the CEMA working group. The knowledge management steps are—

- Assess.
- Design.
- Develop.
- Pilot.
- Implement.

4-104.   The CEWO is responsible for establishing and overseeing the flow of all cyberspace operations and EW-related information throughout the headquarters staff, including higher and lower echelons. The CEWO is accountable for providing IRs to the G-2 or S-2 to attain essential information needed to understand cyberspace and the EMS within an OE. Information acquired from IRs is also crucial to the CEMA section's ability to appropriately integrate and synchronize cyberspace operations and EW with the operations process.

4-105.   The CEMA section and collaborating staff provide meaning to operations by sharing both tacit and explicit knowledge. *Tacit knowledge* is what individuals know; a unique, personal store of knowledge gained from life experiences, training, and networks of friends, acquaintances, and professional colleagues (ATP 6-01.1). All members of the CEMA working group provide knowledge attained from years of operational and strategic experiences, including learned nuances, subtleties, and workarounds from previous operations. *Explicit knowledge* is codified or formally documented knowledge organized and transferred to others through digital or non-digital means (ATP 6-01.1). Explicit knowledge is authoritative knowledge containing standards attained from, by not implicit to, policies, regulations, doctrine. For more information on the knowledge management process, refer to ATP 6-01.1.

Other books we publish on Amazon.com

Army Methodologies Used for Planning Activities

Cyberspace operations and electromagnetic warfare require detailed planning synchronized with the planning activities of the operations process. During the planning activities, units typically rely on the two most common Army methodologies to plan for operations: The Army design methodology and military decision-making process. This appendix discusses how cyberspace operations and electromagnetic warfare are integrated and synchronized into the operations process and integrating processes using the Army design methodology and the military decision-making process.

SECTION I – PLANNING METHODOLOGIES

A-1. Planning is a continuous learning activity, and though it may start an iteration of the operations process, it does not stop with the production of a plan or order. Planning may be highly structured, involving the commander, staff, subordinate commanders, and others who develop a fully synchronized plan or order. Planning may also be less structured, involving only the commander and select staff.

A-2. Planning techniques and methods vary depending on the circumstances. Planners may plan forward, starting with the present condition and layout potential decisions and actions in sequential order until they reach the desired end state. Planners sometimes plan in reverse, beginning with the envisioned end state and working backward. Planning methods may be analytical, as in the military decision-making process, or more systemic, as in the Army design methodology. The Army design methodology and military decision-making process are the Army's two most commonly practiced methodologies when conducting planning activities. A product of planning is an OPLAN or OPORD.

> *Note.* The following discussion only describes integrating and synchronizing cyberspace operations and EW through the operations process using integrating processes. This appendix does not discuss how the integrating processes or other missions are incorporated into the operations process. For more information on how the integrating processes and other missions integrate into the operations process, refer to the proponent doctrine for each process.

ARMY DESIGN METHODOLOGY

A-3. The *Army design methodology* is a methodology for applying critical and creative thinking to understand, visualize, and describe problems and approaches to solving them (ADP 5-0). When problems are challenging to identify, the end state of the operation is unclear, or a COA is not self-evident; commanders employ Army design methodology. Army design methodology is particularly useful as an aid to conceptual planning, but it must be integrated with the detailed planning, typically associated with the military decision-making process, to produce executable OPLANs and OPORDs. The CEMA section participates as part of the design methodology team, when directed, for insight on the complexities of cyberspace operations and EW concerns. Army design methodology assists in the conceptual planning of integrating and synchronizing cyberspace operations and EW with the concept of operations. Army design methodology is systemic (only focusing on individual parts of a complete plan) and requires integration with a more detailed and analytical planning methodology, such as the military decision-making process, to produce executable OPLANs and OPORDs. Unlike the military decision-making process, Army design methodology does not have set prescribed steps. However, several activities are associated with Army design methodology. They are—

- Framing an OE.
- Framing problems.
- Developing an operational approach.
- Reframing when necessary.

A-4. When framing the OE, the CEMA working group focuses on providing the design methodology team a full understanding of the current conditions of cyberspace and the EMS in which an upcoming mission will occur. By framing the OE, the commander and staff can determine the desired end state for the OE, including desired conditions in cyberspace and the EMS necessary to conduct operations.

A-5. After the commander and staff determine the desired end state for the OE, the CEMA working group begins framing problems of identifiable cyberspace and EMS-related obstacles impeding progress toward that desired end state. Once each problem has been framed, and broad actions developed to prevent or mitigate each problem, the CEMA working group can now assist the commander in developing an operational approach to solving all issues identified. Upon completing an operational approach to resolve problems, the commander and staff begin a more refined planning process such as the military decision-making process.

THE MILITARY DECISION-MAKING PROCESS

A-6. The military decision-making process is the most common iterative planning methodology used to understand the situation and mission, develop a COA, and produce an OPLAN or OPORD. The commander, CEMA section, and staff integrate cyberspace operations and EW throughout the military decision-making process. The CEMA section relies heavily on collaboration with staff and support in planning, integrating, and synchronizing cyberspace operations and EW throughout the military decision-making process as members of the CEMA working groups.

A-7. The military decision-making process consists of the following seven steps—

- Step 1: Receipt of the mission.
- Step 2: Mission analysis.
- Step 3: COA development.
- Step 4: COA analysis.
- Step 5: COA comparison.
- Step 6: COA approval.
- Step 7: Orders production, dissemination, and transition.

STEP 1: RECEIPT OF MISSION

A-8. Commanders initiate the military decision-making process upon receipt or in anticipation of a mission. This step alerts the CEMA section to establish the CEMA working group consisting of staff members contributing to the integration and synchronization of cyberspace operations and EW into the overall operation. The alert enables the CEMA working group to determine the amount of time available for planning, integrating, and synchronizing cyberspace operations and EW with the overall operation and decide on a planning approach to accomplish the task. The CEMA working group gather necessary tools in preparation for Step 2: Mission Analysis. These tools include—

- Cyberspace operations and EW specific current running estimates, including—
  - Facts regarding cyberspace and the EMOE in the assigned AO.
  - Assumptions regarding cyberspace and the EMOE in the assigned AO.
  - Friendly forces' cyberspace and EW capabilities operating in the AO, including available technical data.
  - Outgoing unit's high payoff target list recommendations.
  - Outgoing unit's detailed frequencies of interest.
  - Enemy activities and cyberspace and EW capabilities, including available technical data.
  - Conclusion and recommendations for meeting the commander's cyberspace operations and EW-related objectives.

- Relevant publications, including Army and joint regulations and doctrine on cyberspace operations and EW.
- All documents related to the mission and AO, including the higher headquarters' OPLAN or OPORD, maps and terrain products, known friendly, neutral, and enemy cyberspace and EW capabilities used in the AO, and operational graphics.
- Higher headquarters and other organizations' intelligence and assessment products on friendly, neutral, threat cyberspace and EW activities, and cyberspace and EW-related military terrain aspects in the AO.

A-9. The CEMA working group begin updating cyberspace operations and EW specific running estimates, especially the status of friendly forces, cyberspace and EW capabilities, and key civil considerations when employing cyberspace and EA operations. A *running estimate* is the continuous assessment of the current situation used to determine if the current operation is proceeding according to the commander's intent and if planned future operations are supportable (ADP 5-0).

A-10. The CEMA working group conducts an initial assessment of time and resources available to plan, prepare, and begin execution of cyberspace operations and EW that may potentially support the commander's concept of operation. Table A-1, below, illustrates the actions and key outputs of the CEMA working group during Step 1: receipt of the mission.

Table A-1. Step 1: Receipt of mission

Key Inputs	Process	Key Outputs
• Commander's alert and initial guidance.	• Gather tools relevant to cyberspace operations and electromagnetic warfare.	• Update to cyberspace operations and electromagnetic warfare relevant running estimate.
• Operation plans or operation orders from higher headquarters.	• Update cyberspace operations and electromagnetic warfare relevant running estimates.	• Consolidation of other relevant cyberspace operations and electromagnetic warfare tools.
• Higher headquarters provide cyberspace operations and electromagnetic warfare relevant tools, including current running estimates.	• Provide cyberspace operations and electromagnetic warfare input for commander's initial guidance and warning order.	

STEP 2: MISSION ANALYSIS

A-11. The military decision-making process continues with an assessment of the situation called mission analysis. The commander and staff, informed by subordinate and adjacent commanders and joint and mission partners, gather, analyze, and synthesize information to understand the current conditions of the OE. Through mission analysis, the commander and staff can attain situational awareness of the OE. They can then identify *what* the command must accomplish, *when* and *where* operations must take place and the *why* the operation is required.

A-12. The CEMA section analyzes and synthesizes the cyberspace operations and EW tools gathered during Step 1: Receipt of Mission to attain situational awareness of cyberspace, the EMS, and the information environment in the AO in which the operation will take place. The CEMA working group analyzes the higher headquarters OPLAN or OPORD, focusing on Annex C, Appendix 12. The G-6 or S-6 focuses on Annex H. By analyzing higher headquarters' OPLAN or OPORD, the CEMA section can attain an understanding of the unit's cyberspace operations and EW-related tasks, purpose, and how they contribute to the mission, commander's intent, and concept of operations. During mission analysis, the CEMA working group uses higher headquarters' OPLAN or OPORD to attain awareness of available cyberspace and EW assets, the timeline of the operation, and cyberspace and EW missions occurring in the AO by other Services and unified action partners.

A-13. During mission analysis, the G-2 or S-2 leads the IPB to analyze mission variables of the enemy, terrain, weather, and civil considerations in an area of interest. The CEMA section collaborates with the G-2 or S-2 throughout the IPB to help analyze the effect of those mission variables on cyberspace operations and EW. This collaboration includes using tools and products received from higher headquarters to conduct an initial terrain analysis.

A-14. The IPB process identifies critical gaps in the commander's knowledge of the OE, including gaps in one or more of cyberspace and EMS-related military aspects of terrain and the overall information environment. The commander and staff use these gaps as a guide to establishing their IRs or IPB products. The CEMA working group establishes the initial IRs to attain information on recognized gaps identified during terrain analysis to define cyberspace and the EMOE. IPB products provided by the CEMA section, in conjunction with IPB products established by other staffs during mission analysis for other operations, results in—

- The drafting of initial priority intelligence requirement.
- The production of a complete modified combined obstacle overlay with cyberspace and EW considerations within the assigned AO
- The production of threat overlays, including cyberspace and EW considerations within the assigned AO.
- A list of cyberspace and EW-related HVTs.
- Identifying cyberspace and EMS-related military aspects of the terrain.
- Unrefined event templates and matrices that include cyberspace and EW considerations.

A-15. The CEMA working group analyzes the higher headquarters' OPLAN or OPORD and the higher commander's guidance to determine their specified and implied cyberspace operations and EW-related tasks. A *Specified task* is a task specifically assigned to a unit by its higher headquarters (FM 6-0). An *implied task* is a task that must be performed to accomplish a specified task or mission but is not stated in the higher headquarters' order (FM 6-0). The *what* of a mission statement in higher headquarters' OPLAN or OPORD is always a task. The CEMA section determines essential tasks from the specified and implied cyberspace and EW-related tasks included in the unit's recommended mission statement. An *essential task* is a specified or implied task that must be executed to accomplish the mission (FM 6-0).

A-16. The CEMA section examines the unit's current task organization of cyberspace and EW assets, command and support relationships for augmentation, and status of current cyberspace and EW capabilities and their limitations. The CEMA section also analyzes the cyberspace and EW capabilities of adjacent, joint, mission partners, and civilian organizations operating within the unit's AO. This analysis results in the CEMA section determining if the unit has the assets needed to complete all specified, implied, and essential tasks and to identify other cyberspace and EW resources required to fulfill those tasks for mission success. The CEWO informs the commander of all identified cyberspace and EW resource gaps that need forwarding to higher headquarters. The CEMA section provides the commander with any deviations necessary from the standard task organization to consider when developing planning guidance.

A-17. The CEMA working group identifies any constraints placed on the unit regarding cyberspace operations and EW. A *constraint* is a restriction placed on the command by a higher command (FM 6-0). A constraint dictates an action or inaction, thus restricting the freedom of action of a subordinate command. Constraints are in paragraph 3 of the OPLAN or OPORD. The CEMA section should be aware of cyberspace and EW-related limitations, including spectrum usage, the types of cyberspace and EW capabilities allowed, and cyberspace operations and EW-related authorizations delegated and not delegated to the unit commander.

A-18. The CEMA working group gathers critical facts based on analyzing the mission and operational variables provided through the IPB process and from adjacent, higher, joint organizations and mission partners. This information helps with developing assumptions of cyberspace and the EMOE throughout the assigned AO. A fact is a statement of truth, or a statement thought to be true at the time. An assumption is a supposition on the current situation or a presupposition on the future course of events, either or both assumed to be true in the absence of positive proof, necessary to enable the commander in the process of planning to complete an estimate of the situation and make a decision on the COA. In the absence of facts, the CEMA working group establishes assumptions of cyberspace and the EMS within their assigned AO. These assumptions include potential threat cyberspace and EW capabilities operating within the assigned AO.

A-19. The CEMA section uses risk management to prioritize cyberspace security. The CEMA section collaborates with the G-6 or S-6 spectrum manager to review the joint restricted frequency list and mitigate apparent and potential frequency and network conflictions. The CEMA section employs EP to mitigate electromagnetic environmental effects, electromagnetic compatibility issues, implement electromagnetic hardening, and electromagnetic masking.

A-20. During mission analysis, the CEMA working group identifies cyberspace and EW-related gaps in the information received from higher headquarters, adjacent and joint units, and mission partners. These gaps are provided to the commander and added to the commander's critical information requirements, which falls into two categories: PIRs and friendly force information requirement(s). A *priority intelligence requirement* is an intelligence requirement, stated as a priority for intelligence support that the commander and staff need to understand the adversary or other aspects of the operational environment (FM 6-0). A *friendly force information requirement* is information the commander and staff need to understand the status of friendly force and supporting capabilities (FM 6-0).

A-21. The CEMA section works closely with the G-3 or S-3 and G-2 or S-2 in developing the initial information collection plan. The CEMA section also works with these sections to adjust the information collection effort to answer IRs necessary in developing an effective plan. The CEMA section nominates cyberspace and EW-related PIRs and FFIRs to the commander as contributing products to the information collection plan.

A-22. The initial information collection plan sets reconnaissance, surveillance, and intelligence operations in motion. The G-2 or S-2 bears overall responsibility for the information collection plan and works closely with the G-3 or S-3, and attains information to support the IPB process by synchronizing available SIGINT products to satisfy CCIRs and IRs and to provide the commander with intelligence throughout the OE for continuous situational awareness.

A-23. As more information becomes available, the CEMA section updates cyberspace operations and EW-related running estimates that will result in recommended adjustments to the overall plan of operation. The CEMA section considers using available time by comparing the needed time to accomplish cyberspace operations and EW-related tasks to the higher headquarters' timeline and determine the possibility of mission accomplishment in the allotted time. The CEMA section makes the necessary adjustments to the plan of operations in an attempt to stay within timeline parameters and inform the commander of any task that cannot be accomplished with the allotted time, especially those tasks deemed critical or essential. The commander uses this information to determine accepted risks and to inform higher headquarters of gaps identified because of timeline constraints.

A-24. The CEMA section contributes to developing COA evaluation criteria by establishing standards used to measure the effectiveness and efficiency of cyberspace operations and EW discussed in one COA relative to other COAs. Developing these criteria during mission analysis helps to eliminate bias before COA analysis and comparisons. Table A-2, page A-6, illustrates the actions and key outputs of the CEMA working group during Step 2: mission analysis.

Table A-2. Step 2: Mission analysis

Key Inputs	Process	Key Outputs
• Commander's initial guidance. • Higher headquarters tools, including operation plan/order, and intelligence and knowledge products. • Knowledge products from other organizations. • Army design methodology products (unless commander decided to go straight into the military decision making process).	• Analyze cyberspace operational and electromagnetic warfare related information from higher headquarters tools. • Participate in mission analysis briefing. • Participate in intelligence preparation of the battlefield process. • Analyze higher headquarters operation plan/order for specified, implied, essential cyberspace operations and electromagnetic warfare related tasks. • Examine the unit's current task organization of cyberspace and electromagnetic warfare assets. • Examine cyberspace and electromagnetic warfare capabilities of adjacent, joint, mission partners, and civilian organizations in assigned area of operations. • Gather critical facts to develop assumptions. • Begin the risk management process relating to cyberspace operations and electromagnetic warfare. • Continued analysis of cyberspace operations and electromagnetic warfare related information received from higher headquarters, adjacent and joint units, and unified action partners.	• Understanding of the unit's cyberspace operations and electromagnetic warfare related task, purpose, and contribution to the mission. • Understanding of the available cyberspace and electromagnetic warfare assets and timeline. • Understanding of cyberspace operations and electromagnetic warfare missions of adjacent, supporting, and supported unites in the assigned area of operations. • Attaining full awareness of the assigned area of operations, including mission partners. • Identifying critical gaps in cyberspace, the electromagnetic spectrum, and the information environment within assigned area of operations. • Listing of initial cyberspace operations and electromagnetic warfare related intelligence requirements used for priority intelligence requirements, modified obstacle overlays, threat overlays, identifying high value target, aspect of terrain, unrefined event templates, and matrices. • Identifying specified, implied, and essential tasks used for the recommended mission statement. • Determining assets needed to complete specified, implied, and essential tasks. • Determining additional cyberspace operations and electromagnetic warfare resources required (forward to higher headquarters). • Staying abreast of deviations from normal task organization changes for staff to assist the commander in developing planning guidance for courses of actions development. • Awareness of cyberspace operations and electromagnetic related constraints placed by higher command. • Developing cyberspace operations and electromagnetic warfare related assumptions, including threat cyberspace and electromagnetic warfare capabilities operating in the area of operations, necessary for planning. • Identifying elements of cyberspace operations and electromagnetic warfare that require risk management mitigation. • Identifying cyberspace operations and electromagnetic warfare related gaps in provided information for commander's critical information requirements and development of the information collection plan. • Updating cyberspace operations and electromagnetic warfare relevant running estimates. • Synchronizing and integrating cyberspace and electromagnetic warfare capabilities for information related activities. • Establishing standards for measuring the effectiveness and efficiency of cyberspace operations and electromagnetic warfare used in development of course of action evaluation criteria.

STEP 3: COURSE OF ACTION DEVELOPMENT

A-25. COA development generates options for subsequent analysis and comparison that satisfy the commander's intent and planning guidance. A COA is a broad potential solution to an identified problem. During COA development, the CEMA working group uses the tools received and analyzed from higher headquarters, adjacent and joint units, and unified action partners in conjunction with the commander's intent, planning guidance gathered. The CEMA section contributes to COA development by integrating and synchronizing cyberspace operations and EW into COAs using operational and tactical art. During the development of different COAs, the CEMA working group develops varying methods to integrate, synchronize, and conduct cyberspace operations and EW that is within the commander's intent and planning guidance.

A-26. The CEMA section assists the other staff with examining each prospective COA for validity using the evaluation criteria established during Step 2: Mission Analysis. When considering the validity of each prospective COA, screening criteria should include—

- **Feasibility.** Integrated and synchronized cyberspace operations and EW in the COA that accomplish the mission within the established time, space, and cyberspace and EW resource limitations.
- **Acceptability.** Cyberspace operations and EW integrated and synchronized in the COA balance cost and risk with the advantage gained.
- **Suitability.** Cyberspace operations and EW supports the COA that accomplishes the mission within the commander's intent and planning guidance.
- **Distinguishability.** Cyberspace operations and EW integration, synchronization, and conduct of operation should be different for each COA developed. Differences should include task organizations, cyberspace and EW capabilities, and the use of cyberspace and EW resources from supporting adjacent and joint organizations and unified action partners.
- **Completeness.** Cyberspace operations and EW integrated and synchronized in the COA should incorporate—
  - How cyberspace operations and EW will support the operations process.
  - How cyberspace operations and EW support shaping operations, creating and preserving conditions for success during decisive operations or efforts.
  - How cyberspace operations and EW support sustaining operations, enabling shaping and decisive operations or efforts.
  - How cyberspace operations and EW support the COA, accounting for offensive, defensive, and stability or defense support of civil authorities' tasks.
  - How to perform cyberspace operations and EW specified, implied, and essential tasks to achieve desired conditions in cyberspace and the EMS.
  - How to use cyberspace and EW capabilities to mitigate obstacles, attain access to various avenues of approach (including observation and fields of fire), and protect key terrain in cyberspace and the EMS.

A-27. During COA development, commanders and staff need to understand and appreciate the unpredictable and uncertain nature of the OE. The CEMA section should show this same understanding and appreciation for the unpredictability and uncertainty when supporting the development schemes of cyberspace operations and EW for each COA.

A-28. The CEMA working group assesses cyberspace operations and EW as enablers for combat power (assess relative combat power). *Combat power* is the total means of destructive, constructive, and information capabilities that a military unit or formation can apply at a given time (ADP 3-0). Combat power includes the warfighting functions plus leadership and information.

A-29. The CEMA working group assesses organic and non-organic cyberspace and EW capabilities available for the operation. This assessment assists the CEMA section in making a rough estimate of the ratio of friendly cyberspace and EW capabilities to known enemy cyberspace and EW capabilities.

A-30. The CEMA section compares the combined (organic and non-organic) friendly cyberspace and EW capabilities strengths against enemy cyberspace and EW weaknesses, and vice versa. The CEMA section uses this comparison to identify vulnerabilities in friendly cyberspace and the EMS and gain insight into employing cyberspace operations and EW throughout the assigned AO effectively.

A-31. Based on the commander's guidance and the initial results of relative combat power assessment, the CEMA working group generates different cyberspace operations and EW schemes for developing COAs. The scheme for each COA should indicate opposition toward each likely enemy COA while accounting for essential stability tasks (providing a level of civil security, civil control, and certain essential services). The CEMA working group incorporates brainstorming to generate options to produce the broadest range of choices in establishing cyberspace operations and EW schemes for the COAs. During brainstorming, all members of the working group should remain unbiased and open-minded when developing proposed options.

A-32. The CEMA working group determines the necessary Army and joint doctrinal requirements for cyberspace operations, EW, and supported and supporting operations. The CEMA working group further considers potential cyberspace and EW capabilities of non-organic units and other non-military organizations and agencies.

A-33. The commander and staff develop an operational framework to visualize and describe the application of combat power in time, space, purpose, and resources while developing the concept of operations. The operational framework consists of four components:
- Commanders are assigned an AO for conducting operations.
- Commanders can designate deep, close, support, and consolidation areas to describe the physical arrangement of forces in time and space.
- Within deep, close, support, and consolidation areas, commanders conduct decisive, shaping, and sustaining operations to articulate an operation in terms of purpose.
- Commanders designate the main and supporting efforts to designate the shifting prioritization of resources.

A-34. The CEMA working group brainstorms to generate options on how to provide the necessary cyberspace and EW capabilities to support the four components of the operational framework. Once the CEMA working group has explored possibilities in providing cyberspace operations and EW support for each COA, they examine each COA to determine if it satisfies the screening criteria stated in paragraph A-28, changing, adding, and eliminating COAs as appropriate. The CEMA working group places extensive focus on their developed scheme of cyberspace operations and EW for each COA during the screening. The CEMA working group should avoid creating one good COA among several inadequate COAs when generating options.

A-35. The CEMA working group determines the necessary cyberspace and EW capabilities to employ as enablers for combat power required to support the related tasks and purposes of decisive, shaping, and sustaining operations (the third component of the operational framework). The CEMA working group uses historical planning ratios as a starting point to determine the necessary ratio of friendly cyberspace and EW capabilities to enemy cyberspace and EW capabilities that will result in the desired outcome.

A-36. The CEMA working group also considers the relative cyberspace and EW capabilities necessary to shape the OE, resulting in an initial array that identifies the total amount of cyberspace and EW assets needed to accomplish the mission. The CEMA working group adds this information to the unit's total array of forces used in the commander's broad concept of operations. In the broad concept of operations, the commander describes how arrayed forces accomplish the mission within the commander's intent.

A-37. The CEMA section participates in the COA briefing in which the staff briefs each developed COA to the commander. The CEWO briefs the commander on the cyberspace operations and EW activities and capabilities included in each COA, including effects resulting from operational and mission variables. The CEWO also describes how each scheme of cyberspace operations and EW may result in the desired outcome. After the COA briefing, the commander selects or modifies those selected COAs for continued analysis and issues planning guidance.

A-38. Throughout COA development, the CEMA working group continues to update cyberspace and EW-related running estimates and IPB products (such as overlays, HVTs, and aspects of terrain). Table A-3, page A-9, illustrates the actions and key outputs of the CEMA working group during Step 3: COA development.

A-39. Using the information attained from the collaborative efforts of the CEMA working group, the CEMA section develops cyberspace operations and EW-related statements and sketches for the G-3 or S-3 to incorporate with the statement and supporting sketches for each COA. The statement expresses how cyberspace and operations, and EW support the COA in conducting the combined arms concept. The sketch provides visuals of how cyberspace operations and EW will support forces performing movement and maneuver, including the positioning of forces.

> *Note.* The commander may reject all COAs, accept one or more COAs, or create a new COA by incorporating elements of one or more COAs presented at the COA briefing. If the commander rejects all COAs, the staff starts over at developing new COAs. Accepted or modified COAs move forward to Step 4: Analysis and War-gaming.

Table A-3. Step 3: Course of action development

Key Inputs	Process	Key Outputs

• Commander's mission statement, planning guidance, and intent.
 	
 • Commander's critical information requirements.
 	
 • Updated intelligence preparation of battlefield products.
 	
 • Higher headquarters' cyberspace operations and electromagnetic warfare relevant tools, including updated running estimates.
	• Generate different cyberspace operations and electromagnetic warfare related options for each course of action during development.
	
	 • Assist staff members in examining each developing course of action for validity.
	
	 • Assess cyberspace operations and electromagnetic warfare as functions of combat power.
	
	 • Assess available cyberspace and electromagnetic warfare capabilities (organic and non-organic) available for the operation.
	
	 • Compare combined friendly cyberspace and electromagnetic warfare capabilities against enemy forces and vice versa.
	
	 • Determine necessary Army and joint doctrine requirements.
	
	 • Develop cyberspace and electromagnetic warfare related statements and sketches.
	
	 • Participation in the operational framework development.
	
	 • Participation in the course of action briefing.
		• Integration and validation of an effective scheme of cyberspace operations and electromagnetic warfare for each proposed course of action.
		
		 • Rough ratio of the friendly-to-enemy cyberspace and electromagnetic warfare capabilities.
		
		 • Identification of known vulnerabilities in friendly cyberspace and electromagnetic warfare capabilities.
		
		 • Identification of types of cyberspace and electromagnetic capabilities required to support related tasks and purpose of decisive, shaping, and sustaining operations.
		
		 • Updated cyberspace and electromagnetic warfare related running estimates and intelligence preparation of the battlefield products.
		
		 • Cyberspace and electronic warfare related statements and sketches for course of actions
		    o Provide task organization of supporting cyberspace forces and electronic warfare assets.
		    o Describes how cyberspace and electronic warfare support the broad concept of operations.

STEP 4: COURSE OF ACTION ANALYSIS AND WAR-GAMING

A-40. COA analysis enables the commander and staff to identify difficulties, coordination problems, or probable consequences of planned actions for each COA (accepted or modified during Step 3: COA Development under consideration for approval. During this step, the CEMA working group can identify vulnerabilities in each scheme of cyberspace operations and EW integrated into each accepted or modified COA. These vulnerabilities may include—

- Probable undesirable cyberspace and EW effects to operational and mission variables and vice-versa.
- Potential coordination issues with non-organic organizations for cyberspace operations and EW support.
- Lack of necessary cyberspace and EW capabilities available to attain the desired outcome.

A-41. The CEMA working group uses this newly discovered information to revisit and refine cyberspace and EW-related portions of the COA as discrepancies arrive. COA analysis may also uncover potential execution problems, decisions, and contingencies and may require restarting the planning process.

A-42. A process used to analyze a COA is called war-gaming. War-gaming consists of rules and steps to visualize the flow of operation, given the force's strengths and dispositions, the enemy capabilities, and each possible COA. War-gaming incorporates the mission variables into the scenario to include the impact and requirements of civilians in the AO.

A-43. Through war-gaming, the CEMA working group can visualize the required cyberspace and EW capabilities for related targets in the AO. The CEMA working group can also identify potential vulnerabilities that require cyberspace and EW protection. During war-gaming, the CEMA section assists the G-3 or S-3 in the mission command responsibilities of the war-gaming process by employing and assessing cyberspace operations and EW as a friendly scheme of maneuver. The CEMA section also assists the G-3 or S-3 by inputting cyberspace and EW-related input into the COA statement and supporting sketch for each COA. War-gaming results in refined COAs with updated schemes of cyberspace and EW, a completed synchronization matrix, and decision support templates and matrixes for each COA.

> *Note.* The G-6 or S-6 assesses DODIN operations, spectrum management operations, and their feasibility of each war-gamed COA.

A-44. A synchronization matrix records the results of a war game and depicts how friendly forces for each COA synchronize in time, space, and purpose relating to an enemy COA. The depiction includes the synchronization and integration of cyberspace operations and EW in support of the warfighting functions for each COA. The decision support template and matrix illustrate key decisions and potential actions that are likely to arise during the execution of each COA.

A-45. The CEMA section participates in the war-gaming briefing, delivering a brief to subordinate cyberspace and EW assets to ensure everyone understands the results of the war game. The CEMA section captures all cyberspace and EW-related points of the war game before presenting the briefing to the commander. The CEMA section drafts and submits an RFS for additional cyberspace and EW assets to mitigate vulnerabilities identified during war-gaming. Table A-4, page A-11, illustrates the actions and key outputs of the CEMA working group during Step 4: COA Analysis and War-gaming.

Table A-4. Step 4: Course of action analysis and war-gaming

Key Inputs	Process	Key Outputs
• Revised commander's planning guidance. • Proposed courses of action, including cyberspace operations and electromagnetic warfare solutions. • Updated intelligence preparation of the battlefield products. • Higher headquarters' cyberspace operations and electromagnetic warfare relevant tools, including updated running estimates. • Assumptions from previous steps.	• Participation in war-gaming. • Identify vulnerabilities in the scheme of cyberspace operations and electromagnetic warfare for each course of action war gamed. • Draft development of request for support documents for additional cyberspace and electromagnetic warfare assets. • Provide cyberspace operations and electromagnetic warfare related input for the synchronization matrix.	• Refined scheme of cyberspace operations and electromagnetic warfare for each course of action. • Refined intelligence of the battlefield products used for targeting and overlays. • Additional input to the commander's critical information requirements. • Submitted requests for additional cyberspace and electromagnetic assets. • Updated cyberspace operations and electromagnetic warfare running estimate. • Updated assumptions.

STEP 5: COURSE OF ACTION COMPARISON

A-46. The commander and staff evaluate COAs war-gamed objectively and independently against the evaluation criteria established during Step 2: mission analysis and refined during Step 3: COA development. The goal is to identify the strengths and weaknesses of each COA and select a COA with the highest probability of success, and to develop an OPLAN or OPORD further.

A-47. The CEMA section conducts advantage and disadvantage analysis using a decision matrix to evaluate each COA using the evaluation criteria. The CEMA section highlights the advantages and disadvantages of cyberspace operations and EW for each COA concerning the overall mission. The CEMA section presents those findings to the commander and other staff members. Feedback received in response to the CEMA working group's RFS contributes to the numerous determining factors during the advantage and disadvantage analysis.

A-48. Findings from the advantage and disadvantage analysis conducted by all staff are implemented into a decision matrix for the commander to compare and evaluate COAs thoroughly and logically. A decision matrix assists the commander in making the best decision.

A-49. After analysis and comparison, the staff identifies the preferred COA and makes a recommendation. If the staff cannot reach a decision, the chief of staff (executive officer) decides which COA to recommend. The staff then delivers a decision briefing to the commander with the chief of staff highlighting changes to each COA resulting from the war game. Table A-5, page A-12, illustrates the actions and key outputs of the CEMA working group during Step 5: COA comparison.

Table A-5. Step 5: Course of action comparison

Key Inputs	Process	Key Outputs
• Updated Intelligence preparation of the battlefield products. • Refined courses of action with updated schemes of cyberspace operations and electromagnetic warfare. • Higher headquarters provide cyberspace operations and electromagnetic warfare relevant tools, including current running estimates. • Feedback from submitted cyberspace and electromagnetic warfare requests for support.	• Conduct advantage and disadvantage analysis for each course of action. • Compare and evaluate courses of action with the cyberspace electromagnetic activities section focusing on the scheme of cyberspace and electromagnetic warfare. • Conduct a course of action decision briefing to recommend the staff's preferred course of action.	• Staff's recommended course of action. • Updated cyberspace and electromagnetic warfare running estimate.

STEP 6: COURSE OF ACTION APPROVAL

A-50. After the decision briefing, the commander selects the COA that best accomplishes the mission. If the commander rejects all COAs, the staff restarts the COA development process. If the commander modifies a proposed COA or gives the staff an entirely different COA, the staff war-games the new COA and presents the results to the commander with a recommendation.

A-51. Upon approval of a COA, the commander issues the final planning guidance that includes a refined commander's intent and new CCIRs to support the execution of the COA. The final planning guidance also contains any additional guidance on priorities for the warfighting functions, orders preparation, rehearsals, and preparation. It also includes priorities needed to preserve freedom of action and ensure continuous sustainment.

A-52. The commander identifies the acceptable risks in the final planning guidance to gain approval from the higher commander before accepting risks that could affect the higher commander's mission. Based on the commander's decision and final planning guidance, the staff converts the approved COA into the concept of operations and issues a warning order to subordinate commanders. The CEMA section publishes the draft Appendix 12 of Annex C as an attachment to the warning order. The CEMA section continues refining Appendix 12 to Annex C for the OPLAN or OPORD and assists the G-6 or S-6 with Appendixes 1 and 6 of Annex H as appropriate. Table A-6, page A-13, illustrates the actions and key outputs of the CEMA working group during Step 5: COA approval.

Table A-6. Step 6: Course of action approval

Key Inputs	Process	Key Outputs
• Updated cyberspace and electromagnetic spectrum operations running estimate. • Evaluated courses of action. • Staff's preferred course of action. • Higher headquarters provide cyberspace operations and electromagnetic warfare relevant tools, including current running estimates. • Feedback from submitted cyberspace and electromagnetic warfare requests for support.	• Review commander's final planning guidance. • Review the commander's acceptable risk. • Provide cyberspace operations and electromagnetic warfare related input to warning order.	• Commander's final planning guidance. • Approved course of action. • Commander's acceptable risks. • Draft of Annex C, Appendix 12 for warning order. • Assistance to G-6/S-6 with draft of Annex H, Appendices 1 and 6, as appropriate, for warning order. • Refined commander's intent, commander's critical information requirements, and essential elements of friendly information. • Updated assumptions. • Issue of a warning order to subordinate headquarters.

Legend

G-6/S-6   assistant chief of staff, signal

STEP 7: ORDERS PRODUCTION, DISSEMINATION, AND TRANSITION

A-53. The staff turns the approved COA into the OPLAN or OPORD with a clear, concise concept of operations and supporting information. The COA statement becomes the concept of operations for the OPLAN or OPORD. The CEMA section is responsible for the publishing of the final Appendix 12 of Annex C of the OPLAN or OPORD. The CEMA section assists the G-6 or S-6 with Appendixes 1 and 6 of Annex H as appropriate.

A-54. Before the commander approves the OPLAN or OPORD, the staff ensures its consistency and that it is nested with the higher commander's intent through plans and orders reconciliation and crosswalk. The staff conducts a plan and orders reconciliation by conducting a detailed review of the entire OPLAN or OPORD and all attachments, ensuring all staff members are in complete agreement. During reconciliation, the staff explicitly compares the commander's intent, mission, and CCIRs against the concept of operations and the different schemes of support, including the scheme of cyberspace operations and EW. Any discrepancies or gaps in planning receive corrective actions.

A-55. The staff conducts the plans and orders crosswalk by comparing the OPLAN or OPORD with those of the higher and adjacent commanders to achieve unity of effort and ensure the plan meets the highest commander's intent. As with reconciliation, crosswalk also identifies discrepancies or gaps in planning that require corrective actions. Step 7 bridges the transition between the planning activities and the preparations activities of the operations process. The final function of Step 7 is the approval of the OPLAN or OPORD by the commander. The commander signs the OPLAN or OPORD, the G-3 or S-3 disseminate the approved OPLAN or OPORD to the subordinate headquarters, and the commander and staff begin the transition to the preparation activities of the operations process. Table A-7, below, illustrates the actions and key outputs of the CEMA working group during Step 7: orders production, dissemination, and transition.

Table A-7. Step 7: Orders production, dissemination, and transition

Key Inputs	Process	Key Outputs
• Commander-approved course of action. • Higher headquarters provided cyberspace operations and electromagnetic warfare relevant tools, including current running estimates. • Feedback from submitted cyberspace and electromagnetic warfare requests for support. • Draft Annex C, Appendix 12 for the operations plan or order.	• Participation in plans and orders reconciliation. • Participation in plans and orders crosswalk. • Commander's review of the draft operations plan or order.	• Approved operations plan or order with finalized attachments, including Annex C, Appendix 12 and Annex H (G-6/S-6). • Dissemination of approved operations plan or order to subordinate headquarters. • Transition to preparation activities of the operations process.

SECTION II – ANNEX C AND ANNEX H OF THE OPERATIONS PLAN OR ORDER

ANNEX C AND H

A-56. OPLANs, OPORDs, FRAGORDs, and WARNORDs include cyberspace operations and EW information in various paragraphs and Annex C and Annex H. In OPLANs, OPORDs, and FRAGORDs, the scheme of CEMA is discussed in paragraphs 3.g. (Cyberspace Electromagnetic Activities); and 5.g. (Signal). In WARNORDS, cyberspace operations and EW information are in paragraph 5.g. (Signal).

> *Note.* Paragraph 5g (Signal) has information regarding DODIN operations and spectrum management operations-related information.

A-57. Paragraph 3.g. (Cyberspace Electromagnetic Activities) describes how CEMA supports the concept of operations and refers the reader to Appendix 12 (Cyber Electromagnetic Activities) of Annex C (Operations) and Annex H (Signal) as required. Subdivision of Appendix 12 of Annex C and Annex H into the following cyberspace operations and EW-related information is as follows:

- Annex C (Operations), Appendix 12 (Cyberspace Electromagnetic Activities)—CEWO
  - Tab A—Offensive Cyberspace Operations.
  - Tab B—Defensive Cyberspace Operations.
  - Tab C—Electromagnetic Attack.
  - Tab D —Electromagnetic Protection.
  - Tab E—Electromagnetic Support.

- Annex H (Signal)—G-6 or S-6
  - Appendix 1—DODIN operations.
  - Appendix 2—Voice, Video, and Data Network Diagrams.
  - Appendix 3—Satellite Communications.
  - Appendix 4—Foreign Data Exchanges.
  - Appendix 5—Spectrum Management Operations (CEMA assisted).
  - Appendix 6—Information Services.

Note. For more information on OPLANs, OPORDs, FRAGORDs, and WARNORDs, see FM 6-0.

APPENDIX 12 (CYBERSPACE ELECTROMAGNETIC ACTIVITIES) TO ANNEX C (OPERATIONS) TO OPERATION PLANS AND ORDERS

A-58. Appendix 12 to Annex C of OPLANs or OPORDs describes the cyberspace operations and EW divisions (EA, EP, and ES) supporting the commander's concept of operations. The CEWO is overall responsible for publishing Appendix 12 of Annex C and oversees the CEMA section in assisting the G-6 or S-2 with the development of Appendixes 1 and 6 of Annex H. Appendix 12 of Annex C describes the scheme of cyberspace operations and EW and CEMA integration and synchronization processes. It also includes cyberspace operations and EW-related constraints from higher headquarters. Figures A-1 through A-5, beginning on page A-17, illustrate Appendix 12 of Annex C and its associated tabs.

[CLASSIFICATION]

Place the classification at the top and bottom of every page of the OPLAN or OPORD. Place the classification marking at the front of each paragraph and subparagraph in parentheses. See AR 380-5 for classification and release marking instructions.

Copy ## of ## copies
Issuing headquarters
Place of issue
Date-time group of signature
Message reference number

Include the full heading if attachment is distributed separately from the base order or higher-level attachment.

APPENDIX 12 (CYBERSPACE ELECTROMAGNETIC ACTIVITIES) TO ANNEX C (OPERATIONS) TO OPERATION PLAN/ORDER [number] [(code name)]—[issuing headquarter] [(classification of title)]

(U) **References:** *Add any specific references to cyberspace electromagnetic activities, if needed.*

1. **(U)** Situation. *Include information affecting cyberspace operations and electromagnetic warfare (EW) that paragraph 1 of Annex C (Operations) does not cover or that needs expansion.*

a. (U) Area of Interest. *Include information affecting cyberspace and the electromagnetic spectrum (EMS); cyberspace may expand the area of local interest to a worldwide interest.*

b.(U) Area of Operations. *Include information affecting cyberspace and the EMS; cyberspace may expand the area of operations outside the physical maneuver space.*

c.(U) Enemy Forces. *List known and templated locations and cyberspace and EW unit activities for one echelon above and two echelons below the order. Identify the vulnerabilities of enemy information systems and cyberspace and EW systems. List enemy cyberspace and EW operations that will impact friendly operations. State probable enemy courses of action and employment of enemy cyberspace and EW assets. See Annex B (Intelligence) as required.*

d.(U) Friendly Forces. *Outline the higher headquarters' cyberspace electromagnetic activities (CEMA) plan. List plan designation, location and outline of higher, adjacent, and other cyberspace and EW operations assets that support or impact the issuing headquarters or require coordination and additional support. Identify friendly cyberspace and EW operations assets and resources that affect the subordinate commander. Identify friendly forces cyberspace and EMS vulnerabilities. Identify friendly foreign forces with which subordinate commanders may operate. Identify potential conflicts within the EMS, especially for joint or multinational operations. Deconflict and prioritize spectrum distribution.*

e.(U) Interagency, Intergovernmental, and Nongovernmental Organizations. *Identify and describe other organizations in the area of operations that may impact cyberspace and EW operations or implementation of cyberspace and EW operations specific equipment and tactics. See Annex V (Interagency) as required.*

[page number]
[CLASSIFICATION]

Figure A-1. Annex C, Appendix 12

[CLASSIFICATION]

f.(U) Third Party. *Identify and describe other organizations, both local and external to the area of operations that have the ability to influence cyberspace and EW operations or the implementation of cyberspace and EW operations specific equipment and tactics. This category includes criminal and non-state sponsored rogue elements.*

g.(U) Civil Considerations. *Describe the aspects of the civil situation that impact cyberspace and EW operations. See Tab C (Civil Considerations) to Appendix 1 (Intelligence Estimate) to Annex B (Intelligence) and Annex K (Civil Affairs Operations) as required.*

h.(U) Attachments and Detachments. *List units attached or detached only as necessary to clarify task organization. List any cyberspace and EW operations assets attached or detached, and resources available from higher headquarters. See Annex A (Task Organization) as required.*

i.(U) Assumptions. *List any CEMA specific assumptions.*

2. (U) **Mission**. *State the commander's mission and describe cyberspace operations and EW to support the base plan or order.*

3.   (U) **Execution.**

a.   Scheme of Cyberspace Electromagnetic Activities. *Describe how cyberspace and EW operations support the commander's intent and concept of operations. Establish the priorities of support to units for each phase of the operation. State how cyberspace and EW effects will degrade, disrupt, deny, and deceive the enemy. State the defensive and offensive cyberspace and EW measures. Identify target sets and effects, by priority. Describe the general concept for the integration of cyberspace and EW operations. List the staff sections, elements, and working groups responsible for aspects of CEMA. Include the cyberspace and EW collection methods for information developed in staff section, elements, and working groups outside the CEMA section and working group. Describe the plan for the integration of unified action and nongovernmental partners and organizations. See Annex C (Operations) as required. This section is designed to provide insight and understanding of the components of cyberspace and EW and how these activities are integrated across the operational plan. It is recommended that this appendix include an understanding of technical requirements.*

This appendix concentrates on the integration requirements for cyberspace and EW operations and references appropriate annexes and appendixes as needed to reduce duplication.

(1) (U) Organization for Combat. *Provide direction for the proper organization for combat, including the unit designation, nomenclature, and tactical task.*

(2) (U) Miscellaneous. *Provide any other information necessary for planning not already mentioned.*

b.   (U) Scheme of Cyberspace Operations. *Describe how cyberspace operations support the commander's intent and concept of operations. Describe the general concept for the implementation of planned cyberspace operations measures. Describe the process to integrate unified action partners and nongovernmental organizations into operations, including cyberspace requirements and constraints. Identify risks associated with cyberspace operations. Include collateral damage, discovery, attribution, fratricide (to U.S. or allied or multinational networks or information), and possible conflicts. Describe actions that will prevent enemy and adversary action(s) to critically degrade the unified command's ability to effectively conduct military operations in its area of operations. Identify countermeasures and the responsible agency. List the warnings, and how they will be monitored. State how the cyberspace operations tasks will destroy, degrade, disrupt, and deny enemy computer networks. Identify and prioritize target sets and effect(s) in cyberspace. If appropriate, state how cyberspace operations support the accomplishment of the operation. Identify plans to detect or assign attribution of enemy and adversary actions in the physical domains and cyberspace. Ensure subordinate units are conducting*

[page number]
[CLASSIFICATION]

Figure A-1. Annex C, Appendix 12 (continued)

[CLASSIFICATION]

defensive cyberspace operations (DCO). Synchronize the CEMA section with the IO officer. Pass requests for offensive cyberspace operations (OCO) to higher headquarters for approval and implementation. Describe how DOD information network operations support the commander's intent and concept of operations. Synchronize DODIN operations with the G-6 (S-6). Prioritize the allocation of applications utilizing cyberspace. Ensure the employment of cyberspace capabilities where the primary purpose is to achieve objectives in or through cyberspace. Considerations should be made for degraded network operations. (Reference appropriate annexes and appendixes as needed to reduce duplication).

(1) (U) DODIN Operations. *Describe how information operations are coordinated, synchronized, and support operations integrated with the G-6 (S-6) to design, build, configure, secure, operate, maintain, and sustain networks. See Annex H (Signal) as required.*

(2) (U) Defensive Cyberspace Operations. *Describe how DCO are conducted, coordinated, integrated, synchronized, and support operations to defend the DODIN-A and preserve the ability to utilize friendly cyberspace capabilities.*

(3) (U) Offensive Cyberspace Operations. *Describe how OCO are coordinated, integrated, synchronized, and support operations to achieve real time awareness and direct dynamic actions and response actions. Include target identification and operational pattern information, exploit and attack functions, and maintain intelligence information. Describe the authorities required to conduct OCO.*

c.   (U) Scheme of Electromagnetic Warfare. *Describe how EW supports the commander's intent and concept of operations. Establish the priorities of support to units for each phase of the operation. State how the EW tasks will degrade, disrupt, deny, and deceive the enemy. Describe the process to integrate and coordinate unified action partner EW capabilities which support the commander's intent and concept of operations. State the electromagnetic attack, electromagnetic protection, and Electromagnetic support measures and plan for integration. Identify target sets and effects, by priority, for EW operations.*

Synchronize with IO officer. See the following attachments as required: Tab C, D, E (Electromagnetic Warfare) to Appendix 12 (Cyberspace Electromagnetic Activities); Appendix 15 (Information Operations of Annex C).

(1) (U) Electromagnetic Attack. *Describe how offensive EA activities are coordinated, integrated, synchronized, and support operations. See Tab C (Electromagnetic Attack) to Appendix 12 (Cyberspace Electromagnetic Activities).*

(2) (U) Electromagnetic Protection. *Describe how defensive EP activities are coordinated, synchronized, and support operations. See Tab D (Electromagnetic Protection) to Appendix 12 (Cyberspace Electromagnetic Activities).*

(3) (U) Electromagnetic Support. *Describe how ES activities are coordinated, synchronized, and support operations. See Tab E (Electromagnetic Support) to Appendix 12 (Cyberspace Electromagnetic Activities).*

d.   (U) Scheme of Spectrum Management Operations. *Describe how spectrum management operations support the commander's intent and concept of operations. Outline the effects the commander wants to achieve while prioritizing spectrum management operations tasks. List the objectives and primary tasks to achieve those objectives. State the spectrum management, frequency assignment, host nation coordination, and policy implementation plan. Describe the plan for the integration of unified action partners' spectrum management operations capabilities. See Annex H (Signal) as required.*

e.   (U) Tasks to Subordinate Units. *List cyberspace and EW operations tasks assigned to each subordinate unit not contained in the base order.*

[page number]
[CLASSIFICATION]

Figure A-1. Annex C, Appendix 12 (continued)

[CLASSIFICATION]

f. (U) <u>Coordinating Instructions</u>. *List cyberspace and EW operations instructions applicable to two or more subordinate units not covered in the base order. Identify and highlight any cyberspace and EW operations specific rules of engagement, risk reduction control measures, environmental considerations, coordination requirements between units, and commander's critical information requirements and critical information that pertain to CEMA.*

4. (U) <u>Sustainment</u>. *Identify priorities of sustainment for cyberspace and EW operations key tasks and specify additional instructions as required. See Annex F (Sustainment) as required.*

a. (U) <u>Logistics</u>. *Use subparagraphs to identify priorities and specific instruction for logistics pertaining to cyberspace and EW operations. See Appendix 1 (Logistics) to Annex F (Sustainment) and Annex P (Host Nation Support) as required.*

b. (U) <u>Personnel</u>. *Use subparagraphs to identify priorities and specific instruction for human resources support pertaining to cyberspace and EW operations. See Appendix 2 (Personnel Services Support) to Annex F (Sustainment) as required.*

c. (U) <u>Health System Support</u>. *See Appendix 3 (Army Health System Support) to Annex F (Sustainment) as required.*

5. (U) <u>Command and Signal</u>.

a. (U) <u>Command</u>.

(1) (U) <u>Location of Commander</u>. *State the location of key cyberspace and EW operations leaders.*

(2) (U) <u>Liaison Requirements</u>. *State the cyberspace and EW operations liaison requirements not covered in the unit's SOPs.*

b. (U) <u>Control</u>.

(1) (U) <u>Command Posts</u>. *Describe the employment of cyberspace and EW operations specific command posts (CPs), including the location of each CP and its time of opening and closing.*

(2) (U) <u>Reports</u>. *List cyberspace operations and EW specific reports not covered in SOPs. See Annex R (Reports) as required.*

c.(U) <u>Signal</u>. *Address any cyberspace operations and EW specific communications requirements. See Annex H (Signal) as required.*

ACKNOWLEDGE: *Include only if attachment is distributed separately from the base order.*

[Commander's last name]
[Commander's rank]

*The commander or authorized representative signs the original copy of the attachment. If the representative signs the original, add the phrase **For the Commander**. The signed copy is the historical copy and remains in the headquarters' files.*

OFFICIAL:

[Authenticator's name]
[Authenticator's position]

[page number]
[CLASSIFICATION]

Figure A-1. Annex C, Appendix 12 (continued)

[CLASSIFICATION]

Use only if the commander does not sign the original attachment. If the commander signs the original, no further authentication is required. If the commander does not sign, the signature of the preparing staff officer requires authentication and only the last name and rank of the commander appear in the signature block.

ATTACHMENTS: *List lower-level attachment (tabs and exhibits). If a particular attachment is not used, place **not used** beside the attachment number. Unit standard operating procedures will dictate attachment development and format. Common attachments include the following:*

APPENDIX 12 (CYBERSPACE ELECTROMAGNETIC ACTIVITIES) TO ANNEX C (OPERATIONS) TO OPERATION PLAN/ORDER [number] [(code name)]- [issuing headquarter] [(classification of title)]

ATTACHMENT: List lower-level attachment (tabs and exhibits)
Tab A - Offensive Cyberspace Operations
Tab B - Defensive Cyberspace Operations
Tab C - Electromagnetic Attack
Tab D - Electromagnetic Protection
Tab E - Electromagnetic Support

DISTRIBUTION: *Show only if distributed separately from the base order or higher-level attachments.*

[page number]
[CLASSIFICATION]

Figure A-1. Annex C, Appendix 12 (continued)

Appendix B

Rules of Engagement and United States Code

This appendix discusses the basic principles and laws (rules of engagement) that govern (or authorize) how commanders, leaders, and personnel conduct cyberspace operations and electromagnetic warfare. The United States Constitution establishes the authority of the President as Commander in Chief of the Armed Forces and gives authority for Congress to fund and regulate the Armed Forces. The President, as Commander in Chief, commands the missions of the Armed Forces and, according to the laws passed by Congress, administers the Armed Forces.

INTRODUCTION

B-1. Army commanders conduct cyberspace operations and EW when directed by the orders of the President of the United States, the Secretary of Defense, and combatant commander(s) designated to perform operations on behalf of the President. These orders fall under the President's authority from Article II, United States Constitution, the Bill of Rights, other executive order(s), presidential policy, DOD and Department of the Army regulations, United States treaty obligations, and other laws (including funding appropriations) passed by Congress.

B-2. Within this legal framework, Army forces conduct cyberspace and EW operations as authorized through executive orders, OPORDs; ROEs; and the policies directed by the Secretary of Defense and the CCDRs. Army forces conduct cyberspace operations and EW as part of the joint force. USCYBERCOM has overall responsibility for overseeing DOD cyberspace operations.

RULES OF ENGAGEMENT

B-3. Commanders, leaders, and personnel must understand and apply the basic principles of the law of armed conflict, rules of engagement, general restrictions, precautions in attack, separation of military activities, special protections, national sovereignty, and environmental considerations as they relate to international law. The law of armed conflict is that part of international law that regulates armed hostilities, which rests on fundamental principles of military necessity, humanity, proportionality, distinction, and honor, all of which apply to how Army forces conduct cyberspace operations and EW.

B-4. Rules of engagement are directives issued by a competent military authority that delineate the circumstances and limitations under which U.S. forces will initiate or continue combat engagement with other forces encountered. Rules of engagement is how the operational commanders regulate armed forces in the context of applicable political and military policy and domestic and international law. Rules of engagement provides a framework that encompasses national policy goals, mission requirements, and the rule of law. Operational commanders make all cyberspace operations and EW-related decisions considering applicable rules of engagement.

B-5. Targeting generally restricted areas, civilian populations, and civilian or protected objects are typically not intentional unless they become threat actors that participate or take a direct part in combat, singularly or as a group. In such cases, these entities lose their protection against direct attack. If the enemy uses civilians as human shields, provided they are not directly involved in hostilities, the civilians are still neutral actors. Commanders must consider civilians used as human shields when determining the level of excessiveness used during a planned attack. The commander ensures to take feasible precautions to reduce the risk of harm to civilians. Normally targeting civilian actors is not accepted; however, IO will conduct target-actor analysis and direct the application of information-related capabilities to include cyberspace operations and EW effects in support of countering misinformation, disinformation, and to inform and influence both adversary and friendly civilian actors.

B-6.   Civilian objects are those objects or locations that are not lawful military objectives. Commanders cannot intentionally target exclusively civilian objects or areas for attack. Furthermore, where such objects or locations are collocated with, or are in proximity to, enemy targets, the responsible commander must conduct a collateral damage analysis. If a protected object or an object on the no-strike list will be affected, commanders must take appropriate steps to mitigate effects or request removal of an object from the no-strike list before lawfully authorizing a strike on the object. The enemy's use of a civilian and protected object or location for military or combat purposes may result in the loss of protected status, rendering it subject to attack.

B-7.   Commanders must take positive steps and precautions to avoid excessive incidental civilian casualties and damage to civilian property. Targeting team members should ensure sound target intelligence and target vetting are employed during target development and in selecting enemy objectives, and not civilian objects, for attacks. Attacks against installations containing structures that affect natural resources-including dams, dikes, and nuclear power facilities, must be carefully considered as creating potentially catastrophic collateral damage.

UNITED STATES CODE

B-8.   Army forces conduct operations directed by the President while adhering to appropriations, authorizations, and statutes of the USC established by Congress. These statutes cover broad areas of law, including domestic security, the regulation of the Armed Forces, Federal crimes, the National Guard, information technology acquisition and service, spectrum management, and intelligence.

B-9.   USC Title 6, Domestic Security, establishes responsibilities for information analysis and infrastructure protection, chief information officers, and cyberspace security oversight. USC Title 6 responsibilities include comprehensive assessments of key resources, critical infrastructure vulnerabilities, and identifying priorities for protective and supportive measures regarding threats.

B-10. USC Title 10, The Armed Forces, enables the Army to organize, train, equip, and provide land, cyberspace operations, and EW units and headquarters. USC Title 10 authorities and restrictions provide context and foundation for how the Secretary of Defense directs military cyberspace operations, EW, and military intelligence operations.

B-11. USC Title 18, Crimes and Criminal Procedure. Army forces conduct cyberspace operations and EW in compliance with Federal law and take measures to ensure operations respect the rights of persons against unlawful searches and seizures according to the 4th Amendment. Coordination with the United States Army Criminal Investigation Command ensures appropriate investigation of criminal activity on the DODIN under Title 18 authorities. The United States Army Criminal Investigation Command is most directly responsible for enforcing USC Title 18 crimes as they affect the DODIN or Army personnel. USC Title 18 includes those crimes conducted in cyberspace.

B-12. USC Title 32, the National Guard, defines Army National Guard units as state military units that are equipped and trained according to Federal statutory authorization. The Army National Guard may conduct missions for their state, but paid for by the Federal government under USC Title 32 if the Secretary of Defense determines the mission is in the interests of the DOD.

B-13. USC Title 40, Ch. 113, Information Technology Acquisition, applies to the Army and all Federal agencies. USC Title 40 establishes the responsibilities of the agency heads and agency chief information officers and guidance for the acquisition of information technology.

B-14. USC Title 44, Public Printing and Documents, establishes responsibilities of agency heads for statutory requirements and authority for ensuring information security and information resource management. Duties and requirements include information security in cyberspace.

B-15. USC Title 47, Telecommunications, prescribes the statutory requirements and authority for access to, and use of, the EMS within the United States and Possessions to Federal agencies. The chief information officer/ G-6, as outlined in AR 5-12, implements national, international, DOD, joint, host-nation, and

Headquarters, Department of the Army spectrum management policies and guidance throughout the Army. In this capacity, the chief information officer/G-6 ensures compliance with Title 47 USC as well as other applicable federal, DOD, and military department EMS governance and policy to minimize radio frequency interference at DOD and Service test ranges and installations for activities such as Global Positioning System testing and EA clearances for training, testing, and evaluation.

B-16. USC Title 50, War and National Defense provide authorities concerning the conduct of both military and intelligence activities of the U.S. Government. Intelligence activities conducted by the United States Government must be appropriately authorized, conform to the Constitution, and conducted under presidential authority. Executive Order 12333 establishes the framework and organization of the intelligence community as directed by the President of the United States. For example, the order identifies the National Security Agency as the lead for SIGINT. DOD policy documents, including DODM 5240.01 establishes DOD policy for the conduct of intelligence operations.

B-17. The Army strictly limits and controls the collection of information on U.S. civilians in the United States. AR 381-10 identifies the types, means, and constraints concerning collection, retention, and dissemination of information in the United States and on U.S. civilians. This regulation applies to cyberspace within the boundaries of the United States and U.S. civilians abroad. Table B-1, page B-4, summarizes USC sections specific to cyberspace roles. USC Title 18 exempts criminal intelligence from some constraints regarding the collection and retention of U.S. civilians' information.

Table B-1. United States Code with specific cyberspace roles

United States Code	Title	Key Focus	Principle Organization	Role in Cyberspace
Title 6	*Domestic Security*	Homeland security	Department of Homeland Security	Security of U.S. cyberspace
Title 10	*Armed Forces*	National defense	Department of Defense	Provide, train, and equip U.S. forces for military operations in cyberspace
Title 18 Title 28	*Crimes and Criminal Procedure* *Judiciary and Judicial Procedure*	Law enforcement	Department of Justice	Crime prevention, apprehension, and prosecution of criminals operating in cyberspace
Title 32	*National Guard*	National defense and civil support training and operations in the U.S.	State Army National Guard, State Air National Guard	Domestic consequence management (if activated for federal service, the National Guard is integrated into the Title 10, Armed Forces
Title 40	*Public Buildings, Property, and Works*	Chief Information Officer roles and responsibilities	All federal departments and agencies	Establish and enforce standards for acquisition and security of information technologies
Title 44	*Public Printing and Documents*	Defines basic agency responsibilities and authorities for information security policy	All federal departments and agencies	The foundation for cybersecurity activities, as outlined in Department of Defense Instruction 8330.01, *Cybersecurity Activities Support to DOD Information Network Operations*
Title 50	*War and National Defense*	A broad spectrum of military, foreign, intelligence, and counterintelligence activities	Commands, Services, and agencies under the Department of Defense and intelligence community agencies aligned under the Office of the Director of National Intelligence	Secure U.S. interests by conducting military and foreign intelligence operations in cyberspace

LAWS AND POLICIES PROTECTING UNITED STATES CITIZENS

B-18. The U.S. does not have a single federal law or policy regulating cyberspace security, information security, or privacy for U.S. citizens. In addition to federal laws and policies, many states within the U.S. have their cyberspace security and data breach notification laws regulated by industry-specific federal regulations and state legislation, with varying scope and jurisdiction. Table B-2, pages B-5 and B-6, describes many federal laws and policies that protect U.S. citizens in cyberspace and the EMS. These laws and policies only protect U.S. citizens nationally. U.S. citizens outside of the United States are subject to the rules of the international country or state in which they reside or visit.

Table B-2. Federal cyberspace security laws and policies protecting United States citizens

Name	Description
Sarbanes-Oxley (SOX) (U.S. Code 15, Chapter 98)	Requires organizations in the U.S. to prove their cybersecurity* credentials. It applies only to public companies.
Securities and Exchange Commission (SEC) Regulation S-P (Code of Federal Regulations 17, Part 248, Subpart A)	Privacy of consumer financial information and safeguarding personal information. A security regulation that requires appropriate cybersecurity* measures. Applies to all U.S. and foreign brokers, dealers, investment companies, and investment advisers that are register with the Securities and Exchange Commission.
Gramm-Leach-Bliley Act (GLBA) (U.S. Code 15, Subchapter I)	Is both an information security and privacy law, and applies to financial institutions and includes banks, insurance companies, security firms, non-bank mortgage lenders, auto dealers, and tax preparers.
Federal Trade Commission Act, Section 5 (U.S. Code 15, Section 45)	Both an information security regulation requiring appropriate cybersecurity measures and a privacy law. Applies to almost every organization in the U.S. with the exception of banks and common carriers
Health Insurance Portability and Accountability Act (HIPAA) (Code of Federal Regulations 45, Part 160 and 164	Has security, privacy, and breach notification rules. Applies to health care providers, health plans, health care clearinghouses, and in certain cases, business associates of these types of businesses called covered entities. As a result, this Act can cover organizations as diverse as health insurance companies and pharmaceutical companies.
Defense Federal Acquisition Regulation (DFAR) (Code of Federal Regulations 48, 252.204-7012)	A cybersecurity* regulation that applies to the U.S. Department of Defense contractors. Requires contractors and subcontractors that process, store, or transmit defense information to provide adequate security to safeguard on unclassified information systems.
Children's Online Privacy Protection Act (COPPA) (U.S. Code 15, Chapter 91, and Code of Federal Regulations 16, Part 312)	Is both a privacy and cybersecurity law that applies to websites and online services that are directed at children under the age of 13. Also applies if the operator of the site as actual knowledge that children under the age of 13 are using a website. Regulates how such websites collect, use, and/or disclose personal information from and about children.
Federal Protection Act of 1974 (U.S. Code 5, Chapter 5, Section 552a)	Applies only to agencies of the U.S. Federal Government and governs the collection, maintenance, use, and dissemination of personally identifiable information about individuals that is maintained in systems or records by federal agencies. It prohibits the disclosure of information from a system of records controlled by the federal agency without written consent of the subject individual, unless the disclosure is permitted under one of 12 statutory exceptions. This applies to all individuals that are residents of the U.S. (both lawfully or unlawfully)

Table B-2. Federal cyberspace security laws and policies protecting United States citizens (continued)

Name	Description
Consumer Privacy Protection Act of 2017 (U.S. House of Representatives Bill 4081)	Ensures the privacy and security of sensitive person information, to prevent and mitigate identity theft and to provide notice of security breaches involving sensitive personal information. It also enhances law enforcement assistance and other protections against security breaches, fraudulent access, and misuse of personal information. It applies to organizations that collect, use, access, transmit, store, or dispose of sensitive personally identifiable information of 10,000 or more U.S. citizens during any 12-month period.
Food and Drug Administration (Code of Federal Regulations 21, Part II)	Regulation for the use of electronic records in clinical investigations. Is a cybersecurity law that applies to organizations involved in clinical investigation of medical products, including sponsors, clinical investigators, institutional review boards, and contract research organizations. Many of these operations also fall under the Health Insurance Portability and Accountability Act. It concerns the use of information technology systems of these organizations, including any electronic systems used to create, modify, maintain, archive, retrieve, or transmit records used in clinical investigations.
Commodity Futures Trading Commission Derivatives Clearing Organizations Regulation (Code of Federal Regulations 17, Part 39, Subpart B, and 39.18-System safeguards)	Applies to derivatives clearing organizations (entities acting as a medium for clearing transactions in commodities for future delivery or commodity option transactions).
Electronics Communications Privacy Act and Stored Communications Act (U.S. Code 18, Chapters 119 and 121	Together, are also known as the Wiretap Act and are privacy statutes. Originally designed to limit warrantless surveillance, however, also forbid the intentional use, disclosure, or access to any wire, oral, or electronic communications without authorization.
European-U.S. Privacy Shield	Protects European residents' data held and processed by organizations in the U.S.

Appendix C

Integration with Unified Action Partners

Army forces conduct operations as part of a joint force and routinely work with unified action partners as part of unified action. As such, Army commanders must work with unified action partners throughout the operations process. This appendix discusses how commanders and staffs at the joint level integrate cyberspace operations and electromagnetic warfare with various unified action partners.

JOINT OPERATIONS CONSIDERATIONS

C-1. Army operations that involve the use of cyberspace and the Electromagnetic Spectrum (EMS) can have joint implications. Each Service component has cyberspace operations, EMS requirements, and EW capabilities that contribute to an integrated whole, synchronized at the JTF headquarters. The CEMA section ensures that cyberspace operations and EW align with joint IO, spectrum management operations (SMO), and doctrine.

C-2. An Army corps assigned as a JTF headquarters combines its CEMA section, IO officer, and spectrum management chief to establish a JEMSOC. Each Service component subordinate to the JTF headquarters establishes an EMSO cell to fuse with the JEMSOC. A corps or division assigned as a joint force headquarters is also required to establish an EMSO cell by fusing its CEMA section, IO officer, and spectrum management chief.

C-3. The theater campaign plan guides the planning of cyberspace and EW capabilities. The Army contributes an integrated cyberspace and EW plan to support joint operations.

Note. For more information on joint IO, see JP 3-13. For more information on joint spectrum management operations, see JP 3-85.

INTERAGENCY AND INTERGOVERNMENTAL CONSIDERATIONS

C-4. Army commanders must consider the unique capabilities, structures, and priorities of interagency and intergovernmental partners before conducting cyberspace operations and EW. Successful operations that involve unified action partners require a shared understanding and common objective for the operation.

C-5. Interagency and intergovernmental partners often have command relationships, lines of authority, and planning processes that vary significantly from the Army. Understanding these authorities and processes generally require liaison elements to be in place before operations, as it will likely be too late and ineffective to establish these elements after the fact. Partners often manage tasks through committees, steering groups, and interagency working groups organized along functional lines. The commander is responsible for developing interagency and intergovernmental coordination requirements and establishing a liaison element. The liaison element is similar to that required for multinational operations.

C-6. Interagency and intergovernmental partners sometimes have policies that differ or are more restrictive than the Army's policies. These differences manifest in legal authorities, roles, responsibilities, procedures, and decision-making processes. Commanders ensure interagency and intergovernmental planners understand military capabilities, requirements, operational limitations, liaisons, and legal considerations. Staff integrating these partners into operations must understand the nature of these relationships and types of support that partners can provide. Commanders will likely need to achieve consensus in the absence of a formal command structure to accomplish mission objectives with these organizations.

C-7. Commanders attempt to understand less restrictive authorities and policies that interagency and intergovernmental partners follow. Some of their authorities and policies may consist of applications that may achieve the desired effect more economically, proficiently, or with fewer risks of causing cascading effects. Commanders should be open to using these partner authorities when practical.

MULTINATIONAL CONSIDERATIONS

C-8. Army units executing cyberspace operations and EW within multinational operations require a robust liaison effort. Effective liaison mitigates complications caused by differences in policy and facilitates system integration and information sharing.

C-9. Differences in national standards and laws on sovereignty in cyberspace and the EMS may affect the willingness or the legality of a country's participation in cyberspace operations and EW. Some partners may refuse to participate, while others will enable or undertake their operations separate from the Army commander's mission.

C-10. Connectivity is essential when multi-national forces function in mutual support during combat operations. Interoperability issues may compound connectivity issues. Hardware and software incompatibilities and disparities in standards, information security, and cyberspace security policy may cause gaps in protection or capability that require additional effort to fix. Such issues will likely slow down the collection, dissemination, and sharing of information among partners. Commanders and staffs should anticipate connectivity incompatibilities and disparities before entering a multinational operation.

C-11. Intelligence and information sharing with allies and multinational partners are vital during multinational operations. Special attention and awareness are essential when sharing information due to specific and varying classification sharing policies. When synchronizing cyberspace operations and EW with multinational partners, Army units must ensure adherence to foreign disclosure and cyberspace security procedures. Security restrictions may prevent full disclosure of some cyberspace and EW capabilities or planning, limiting synchronization efforts. Effective synchronization requires access to systems and information at the lowest appropriate security classification level. Commanders are responsible for establishing procedures for foreign disclosure of intelligence information. For more information regarding foreign disclosure, refer to AR 380-10.

NONGOVERNMENTAL ORGANIZATIONS CONSIDERATIONS

C-12. Commanders ensure adherence to cyberspace security procedures when conducting cyberspace operations with nongovernmental organizations. Planning with nongovernmental organizations may be necessary for foreign humanitarian assistance, peace operations, and civil-military operations. Incorporating these organizations into an operation requires the commander to balance the need of the nongovernmental organization for information with operation security. Many nongovernmental organizations may be hesitant to become associated with the military to prevent compromising their status as independent entities. Many seek to maintain this status to avoid losing their freedom of movement or members being at risk in hostile environments. Strategic level planning for the inclusion of nongovernmental organizations into civil affairs operations will likely coordinate cyberspace operations.

HOST-NATION CONSIDERATIONS

C-13. Each nation has sovereignty over its EMS and cyberspace components within its geographic area. The use of a nation's cyberspace and the electromagnetic spectrum (EMS) require coordination and negotiation through formal approvals and certifications. Host nation coordination concerning the use of the EMS is a function of spectrum management operations. Coordinating spectrum use is based mainly on the potential for electromagnetic interference (EMI) with local receivers. This coordination ensures initial spectrum availability and supportability for operations and establishes cyberspace availability, such as bandwidth allocation. The purpose of coordination is to develop an interoperable cyberspace defense capability. Consideration of countries adjacent to a host nation is essential, especially if forces stage, train, or operate within these countries. Likewise, compatibility of protective measures, such as countermeasures systems, is critical to avoid system fratricide.

INSTALLATION CONSIDERATIONS

C-14. Cyberspace operations and EW systems are complex and continually evolving. Warfighter readiness and the ability to fight upon arrival are crucial for a fully capable, ready force. Executing cyberspace operations and EW in a garrison environment presents unique challenges for several reasons. Leaders not physically co-located require the use telephonic or virtual collaboration and coordination. In addition, constraints due to laws, policies, and regulations may limit the use of cyberspace operations and EW on an installation. Specific mission sets for different installations (testing, training, and maintenance) may have special requirements. Additionally, establishing working relationships with garrison organizations such as the Network Enterprise Center is essential. The CEWO works with the installation and host nation agencies to incorporate cyberspace operations and EW training into their organization's exercises.

PRIVATE INDUSTRY CONSIDERATIONS

C-15. Private industry plays a significant role in cyberspace and the EMS. The Army relies on its connectivity with its defense industrial base partners and the private sector for many of its non-warfighting day-to-day functions for support and sustainment. Examples include electronic databases and interfaces for medical services, accounting and finance services, personnel records, equipment maintenance, and logistics functions. Global transport and logistics require data exchange between military and private networks. The Army relies on shipping companies, transportation grid providers, and suppliers as a part of the global transportation system.

C-16. The security and reliability of private industry networks directly affect Department of Defense (DOD) operations. DOD personnel does not administer these networks; however, they are still essential to effective Army operations. Responsibility for these networks falls on the network owners.

C-17. Private industry has proven to be the primary catalyst for advancements in information technology resulting in the DOD becoming increasingly reliant on commercial off-the-shelf technology. Many of these products are developed by, manufactured by, or have components produced by foreign countries. These manufacturers, vendors, service providers, and developers can be influenced by adversaries or unwittingly used by them to provide counterfeit products or products that have built-in vulnerabilities. The DD Form 1494 (*Application for Equipment Frequency Allocation*) process determines the compatibility and interoperability of commercial off-the-shelf systems that use the EMS to support national needs. The DOD follows risk assessments and procedures to ensure proper supply chain management and that the acquisition of software and hardware does not adversely affect the security of the Department of Defense information network (DODIN).

C-18. The DODIN resides on commercial networks as undersea cables, fiber optic networks, telecommunication services, satellite and microwave antennas from local telephone companies, and leased channels from satellites. Many of these commercial networks are under foreign ownership, control, and influence. Reliance on commercial systems makes conducting cyberspace operations and EW vulnerable to access denial, service interruption, communications interception and monitoring, infiltration, and data compromise. Army commanders pursue risk mitigation through adherence to operational security, cyberspace security policies, inspections of vendor-supplied equipment, encryption, and enforcing cybersecurity training requirements.

Other books we publish on Amazon.com

FM 7-22
HOLISTIC HEALTH AND FITNESS
Customer reviews
⭐⭐⭐⭐ 4.7 out of 5

ATP 7-22.02
HOLISTIC HEALTH AND FITNESS
Drills and Exercises
Customer reviews
⭐⭐⭐⭐⭐ 5 out of 5

ATP 7-22.01
HOLISTIC HEALTH AND FITNESS
TESTING
Customer reviews
⭐⭐⭐⭐⭐ 5 out of 5

Army Combat Fitness Test
3.0

Includes:
ACFT 3.0 Scoring Standards
ACFT Performance Categories
Blank Test Scorecards

Appendix D

National, Department of Defense, Army Reserve, and Joint Cyberspace and Electromagnetic Warfare Organizations

Appendix D discusses the national, Department of Defense, and Army Reserve components that support cyberspace operations. This appendix also provides an overview of the United States Cyber Command and its subordinate joint organizations that deliver cyberspace operations and electromagnetic warfare support to Army commanders using cyberspace mission forces.

NATIONAL ORGANIZATIONS

D-1. The United States Constitution establishes the President's authority as Commander in Chief of the Armed Forces and gives authority for Congress to fund and regulate the Armed Forces. The President, as Commander in Chief, commands the missions of the Armed Forces and, according to the laws passed by Congress, administers the Armed Forces.

D-2. The Department of Justice and the Department of Homeland Security also have active roles in national cyberspace security with the DOD. The Department of Justice leads the national effort to investigate cyber-based terrorism, espionage, computer intrusions, and major cyber fraud and is responsible for protecting the commercial domains such as .com, .net, and .org. The Department of Homeland Security is responsible for overseeing the .gov domain's protection and providing assistance and expertise to private sector owners and operators. The DOD protects the .mil domain.

D-3. As part of the Department of Justice, the Federal Bureau of Investigation conducts domestic national security operations, investigates attributes, disrupts cyberspace crimes, and collects, analyzes, and disseminates domestic cyber intelligence. The Department of Homeland Security National Cyber Security Division collaborates with the government, industry, academia, and the international community to make cyberspace security a national priority and shared responsibility. For additional information on Department of Homeland Security responsibilities, see joint doctrine on cyberspace operations.

D-4. Each of the Armed Services has law enforcement and counterintelligence organizations that conduct many of the FBI and Department of Homeland Security functions specific to their appropriate Service. These organizations include the Air Force Office of Special Investigations, the Naval Criminal Investigative Service, the United States Army Criminal Investigation Command, and the United States Army Intelligence and Security Command.

D-5. In coordination with the Department of Homeland Security and responsible state and local officials, the National Guard Bureau coordinates Army National Guard efforts to secure the nation, protect critical state infrastructure, and respond to state cyberspace emergencies. Many states have established cyber response teams capable of responding to cyberspace emergencies in the country.

DEPARTMENT OF DEFENSE ORGANIZATIONS

D-6. DOD uses cyberspace capabilities to shape cyberspace and conduct cyberspace operations missions to defend our nation under the authorities of the Secretary of Defense. Authority for cyberspace operations undertaken by the U.S. Armed Forces derives from the U.S. Constitution and federal law.

D-7. Key sections of the USC that apply to the DOD include Title 10, Armed Forces; Title 50, War and National Defense; and Title 32, National Guard. Appendix D, Table D-1, discusses all applicable USC sections that apply to cyberspace operations. The following agencies provide direct or indirect support for cyberspace operations:

- The National Security Agency and the Central Security Service.
- The Defense Information Systems Agency.
- Defense Intelligence Agency.
- The National Geospatial-Intelligence Agency.
- The National Reconnaissance Office.

NATIONAL SECURITY AGENCY AND CENTRAL SECURITY SERVICE

D-8. The National Security Agency is the U.S. government's lead for cryptology, and its mission encompasses both SIGINT and cyberspace security activities. The Central Security Service conducts SIGINT collection, processing, analysis, production, dissemination, and other cryptology operations assigned by the Director, National Security Agency, and Chief, Central Security Service.

D-9. The National Security Agency and Central Security Service provide SIGINT and cyberspace security guidance and assistance to DOD organizations engaged in collecting, processing, analyzing, producing, and disseminating SIGINT data and information for foreign intelligence and counterintelligence purposes. They support national and departmental missions and provide SIGINT support for military operations as assigned by the Secretary of Defense.

DEFENSE INFORMATION SYSTEMS AGENCY

D-10. The Defense Information Systems Agency is a DOD agency, consisting of military, civilian, and contractors staffed to conduct cyberspace operations and functions similar to cyberspace forces retained by USCYBERCOM, however, at the DOD level. The Defense Information Systems Agency conducts DODIN operations and DCO-IDM missions at the global and enterprise-level within the Defense Information Systems Agency's portion of the DODIN, complying with the commander's, United States Cyber Command directive through the commander, Joint Force Headquarters-Department of Defense Information Network (JFHQ-DODIN).

D-11. The Defense Information Systems Agency provides engineering, architecture, and provisioning support for integrated DODIN operations, including enterprise management, content management, and digital freedom of maneuver. The Defense Information Systems Agency conducts DCO-IDM missions on its portion of the DODIN to mitigate and execute service restoration at the global and enterprise-level, as directed by commander, JFHQ-DODIN.

D-12. The Defense Information Systems Agency acquires and maintains control of all commercial satellite communications (SATCOM) resources (unless the DOD CIO grants a waiver to a requesting organization), while supporting the commander, U.S. Strategic Command, as the SATCOM system expert for commercial SATCOM and DOD gateways. Through commercial SATCOM, the Defense Information Systems Agency provides long-haul communications for all DOD and military Services.

DEFENSE INTELLIGENCE AGENCY

D-13. The Defense Intelligence Agency satisfies military and military-related intelligence requirements of the Secretary and Deputy Secretary of Defense, the Chairman of the Joint Chiefs of Staff, and the Director of National Intelligence. It provides military intelligence contribution to national foreign intelligence and counterintelligence.

D-14. The Defense Intelligence Agency plans, manages, and executes intelligence operations during peacetime, crisis, and war. The Defense Intelligence Agency serves as the DOD lead for coordinating intelligence support to meet CCMD requirements, leads efforts to align analysis and information collection activities with all operations, and links and synchronizes military defense and national intelligence capabilities.

NATIONAL GEOSPATIAL-INTELLIGENCE AGENCY

D-15. The National Geospatial-Intelligence Agency is a combat support agency and an intelligence community (IC) member organization subordinate to the Secretary of Defense, the Under Secretary of

Defense for Intelligence, and the Director of National Intelligence. The National Geospatial-Intelligence Agency produces timely, relevant, and accurate geospatial intelligence (GEOINT) to the joint force and is the primary source for GEOINT analysis, products, data, and services at the national level. The National Geospatial-Intelligence Agency provides advisory tasking recommendations for Service-operated airborne and surface-based GEOINT collection platforms and sensors.

D-16. The NGA provides a National Geospatial-Intelligence Agency support team in direct support to a joint force commander's intelligence operations center and maintains National Geospatial-Intelligence Agency support teams for each of the Services, DOD agencies, and several non-DOD agencies. According to the National Intelligence Priorities Framework, the National Geospatial-Intelligence Agency manages satellite collection requirements and develops distribution protocols for National System for Geospatial Intelligence.

NATIONAL RECONNAISSANCE OFFICE

D-17. The National Reconnaissance Office is a DOD agency and a member of the IC. The National Reconnaissance Office is responsible for research and development, acquisition, launch, deployment, and operation of overhead systems and related data processing facilities that collect intelligence and information to support national and departmental missions and other U.S. Government needs.

RESERVE COMPONENTS

D-18. The Army National Guard and the United States Army Reserve benefit from their associated civilian, academic, industry, and interagency communities to obtain Soldiers with specialized cyberspace operations skills, capabilities, and experience. The active Army leverages the reserve component's cyberspace capabilities by providing expanded capabilities in areas that are often too expensive and too time-consuming for reserve components to handle alone.

NATIONAL GUARD BUREAU

D-19. The National Guard Bureau Chief serves as an advisor to Commander USCYBERCOM. It supports planning and coordination for cyberspace operations and electromagnetic warfare missions requested by CCDRs or the Chairman of the Joint Chiefs of Staff. The National Guard Bureau channels communications between USCYBERCOM and the 50 states, the Commonwealth of Puerto Rico, the District of Columbia, Guam, and the Virgin Islands on all National Guard matters.

ARMY NATIONAL GUARD

D-20. The Army National Guard is a vital component of the Army's total force cyberspace operations capability. It performs cyberspace operations in the 54 joint force headquarters–states supporting both the Army and the states per Title 10 and Title 32 authorities. Their priority is to establish and maintain a secure cyber environment with their respective state through cyberspace operations by protecting critical cyberspace nodes, developing cyberspace operations situational awareness, and providing support to civil authorities for incident response and critical infrastructure protection. The Army National Guard is the Army's expert for protecting critical infrastructure and essential resources. It supports the Army and USCYBERCOM with cyber network operations, cyber support, and cyber warfare capabilities.

UNITED STATES ARMY RESERVE

D-21. The United States Army Reserve provides trained and ready personnel to perform cyberspace operations to support joint, Army, and combatant commander mission requirements. United States Army Reserve personnel bring maturity and depth of experience, providing ready support to current and future operations. Uniquely, the United States Army Reserve will directly link to USCYBERCOM contingency plans, allowing them to mobilize personnel to support ARCYBER plans and operations that support cyberspace operations. The United States Army Reserve is expeditionary and supports ARCYBER and USCYBERCOM with cyberspace capabilities.

UNITED STATES CYBER COMMAND

D-22. The Unified Command Plan and various Secretary of Defense orders grant United States Cyber Command (USCYBERCOM) the coordinating authority for all DOD cyberspace operations, including those operations to operate, secure, and defend the DODIN. USCYBERCOM accomplishes its missions within three primary lines of operation: secure, operate, and defend the DODIN; defend the nation from attack in cyberspace; and provide cyberspace support as required by a combatant commander. USCYBERCOM directs the security operations and defense of the DODIN using directive authority for cyberspace operations. When directed, USCYBERCOM also conducts military cyberspace operations external to the DODIN in support of national objectives. Refer to JP 3-12 for more information on USCYBERCOM roles and responsibilities.

D-23. Cyberspace operations are conducted by cyberspace forces consisting of both military and civilian personnel. DOD cyberspace forces include forces assigned to USCYBERCOM through the global force management process, Service-retained forces, and reserve component forces. Cyberspace forces also include personnel that perform cybersecurity service provider roles established by the Services and DOD agencies to protect segments of the DODIN. Cybersecurity service providers are generally DOD certified civilians and contractors who perform DODIN protection services such as analytics, infrastructure support, incident response, auditing, and service provider management.

CYBER MISSION FORCE

D-24. The commander, United States Cyber Command exercises combatant command authority over the cyber mission force. The commander, United States Cyber Command uses cyber mission force units to conduct national strategic missions or assigns units to support combatant commander missions through a JFHQ-C. The cyber mission force is a subset of the DOD's total force for cyberspace operations. The cyber mission forces consists of three types of elements:

- Cyber combat mission force.
- Cyber protection force.
- Cyber national mission force (CNMF).

Cyber Combat Mission Force

D-25. The cyber combat mission force conducts OCO and related technical and analytical activities in support of geographic or functional CCMD operations. When authorized and directed, the cyber combat mission force conducts cyberspace attacks in neutral and enemy cyberspace to create effects against threat capabilities. The cyber combat mission force consists of combat mission teams and combat support team(s).

D-26. Combat mission teams are tactical teams that conduct cyberspace reconnaissance and cyberspace attacks in neutral and enemy cyberspace. Combat cyber teams are technical teams that support combat mission teams through intelligence analysis, cyberspace capability development, linguist support, and planning.

Cyber Protection Force

D-27. The cyber protection force conducts DCO-IDM within the DODIN or, when authorized and directed, in friendly cyberspace beyond the DODIN. The cyber protection force consists of cyber protection team(s) (CPT) organized, trained, and equipped to defend assigned cyberspace in coordination with and supporting segment owners, cybersecurity service providers, and users. The types of CPTs are—

- **National CPTs.** Assigned to and directed by Cyber National Mission Force-Headquarters (CNMF-HQ).
- **DODIN CPTs.** Assigned to and directed by Joint Force Headquarters-Department of Defense information network.
- **CCMD CPTs.** Assigned to and directed by CCMDs.
- **Service CPTs.** Assigned to and directed by their assigned Service cyberspace component.

Cyber National Mission Force

D-28. The CNMF conducts DCO against cyberspace threats based on USCYBERCOM and national priorities. The CNMF may conduct DCO within the DODIN or, when authorized, outside of the DODIN in friendly cyberspace. When authorized and directed the CNMF conducts DCO-RA in neutral and enemy cyberspace. The CNMF consists of national mission teams, national support team(s), and national CPTs.

D-29. National mission teams are tactical teams that conduct DCO-RA. NSTs support national mission teams with intelligence analysis, cyberspace capability development, linguist support, and planning. National CPTs conduct national-level DCO-IDM that can extend to defend non-DOD mission partners or critical infrastructure networks when ordered by the Secretary of Defense. The CNMF is assigned to and directed by the CNMF-HQ. Table D-1, below, outlines the interrelationship between cyber mission force elements, associated cyberspace operations and actions, and typical operating locations in friendly, neutral, and enemy cyberspace.

Table D-1. Elements of the cyber mission force and their associated teams

Type of Cyberspace Operation	Cyberspace Force Conducting the Operation	Location in Cyberspace	Type of Cyberspace Actions
DODIN Ops	Service retained cyber mission forces	The DODIN	Cyberspace security
OCO	Cyber combat mission force consisting of combat mission teams supported by combat support teams	Neutral and adversary cyberspace	Cyberspace attack and exploitation
DCO-IDM (DODIN)	Cyber protection force consisting of Service, DODIN, and CCMD CPTs	Friendly cyberspace	Cyberspace defense
DCO-IDM (non-DODIN)	Cyber protection force consisting of national CPTs	Non-DODIN friendly cyberspace	Cyberspace defense
DCO-RA	CNMF consisting of NMTs supported by national support teams	Neutral and adversary cyberspace	Cyberspace attack and exploitation

Legend		
CCMD	combatant command	DODIN	Department of Defense information network
CNMF	cyber national mission force		
CPT	cyber protection team	DODIN Ops	Department of Defense information network operations
DCO-IDM	defensive cyberspace operations-internal defense measures	NMT	national mission team
DCO-RA	defensive cyberspace operations-response actions	OCO	offensive cyberspace operations

UNITED STATES CYBER COMMAND SUBORDINATE ELEMENTS

D-30. Figure D-1 on page D-6, illustrates the allocation of teams from the cyber mission force to USCYBERCOM's subordinate elements and combatant commands. USCYBERCOM subordinate elements are —

- CNMF-HQ.
- JFHQ-DODIN.
- JFHQ-C (total of four).
- Service cyberspace component commands.

Note. The commandant of the Coast Guard is the only Service that retains operational control over all of its cyberspace forces per a memorandum of agreement between the DOD and the Department of Homeland Security. The Commander, Coast Guard Cyber Command is not dual-hatted as a commander of a JFHQ-C.

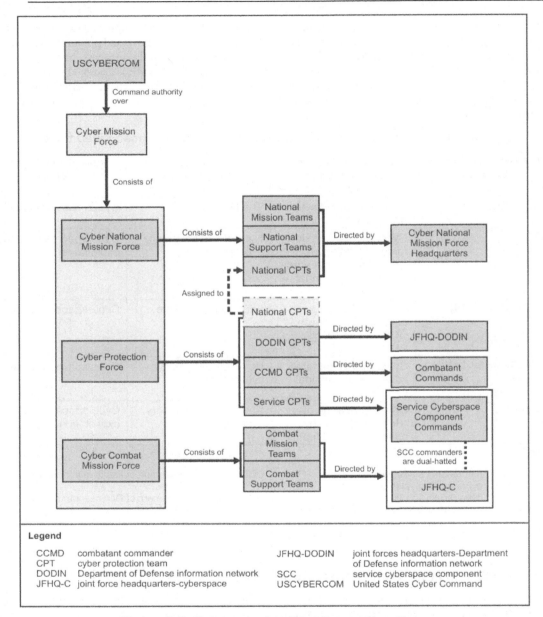

Figure D-1. Cyber mission force team allocations

Cyber National Mission Force-Headquarters

D-31. The CNMF-HQ defends the nation's cyberspace through the planning, coordination, execution, and oversight of DCO missions against threat actors in cyberspace. The CNMF-HQ employs national CPTs for internal threats to critical non-DODIN friendly cyberspace. The CNMF commander has operational control of national mission teams, NSTs, and national CPTs.

Joint Force Headquarters-Department of Defense Information Network

D-32. In coordination with all CCDRs, JFHQ-DODIN directs and conducts global DODIN operations and DCO-IDM. The JFHQ-DODIN is the focal point for interagency deconfliction of global JFHQ-DODIN and DCO-IDM activities that may affect more than one DOD component. USCYBERCOM has delegated operational control of SCCs to JFHQ-DODIN for defense of the DODIN. USCYBERCOM has also delegated directive authority for cyberspace operations to the CDR, JFHQ-DODIN, which enables JFHQ-DODIN to task Services and other DOD entities to take cyberspace security and cyberspace defense actions throughout the DODIN.

Service Cyberspace Component Commands

D-33. USCYBERCOM and JFHQ-DODIN conduct DODIN operations and DCO-IDM through subordinate SCCs. In coordination with or under the direction of the commander, JFHQ-DODIN, SCCs conduct DODIN operations and DCO-IDM within their respective Service-maintained portion of the DODIN. JFHQ-DODIN delegates directive authority for cyberspace operations to the SCCs for actions within their maintained portion of the DODIN. For the Army, CG, ARCYBER directs DODIN operations and DCO-IDM on the DODIN-A. Each Service cyberspace component commander, other than the commander of Coast Guard Cyber Command, is dual-hatted by the commander, United States Cyber Command to also command of one of the four JFHQ-Cs.

Joint Force Headquarters-Cyberspace

D-34. JFHQ-Cs analyze, plan, and execute OCO missions in general support of one or more CCDRs. JFHQ-Cs refine cyberspace intelligence requirements, provide operational command and control of combat mission teams and combat cyber teams, and support the integration of OCO into CCDRs plans and orders.

D-35. Army commanders should understand that the JFHQ-C supporting their operation would not necessarily be JFHQ-C (Army). Because JHFQ-Cs are tied by support relationships to specific CCMDs, the JFHQ-C supporting an Army unit will depend on which CCMD the unit is assigned or attached to for a given mission. For instance, operations in support of U.S. Indo-Pacific Command would be conducted through JFHQ-C (Navy), while operations in support of U.S. Central Command would be conducted through ARCYBER acting as JFHQ-C (Army).

COMBATANT COMMANDS

D-36. USCYBERCOM has assigned CCMD CPTs to geographic and functional CCDRs to conduct DCO-IDM missions within their area of responsibility (AOR). CCMDs have organic joint cyberspace centers and receive direct support from cyberspace operations-integrated planning elements provided by USCYBERCOM.

D-37. CCDRs use assigned CPTs to conduct DCO-IDM on networks and systems operated and maintained by the CCMD. However, forces under the command of CCDRs often operate on Service-maintained networks and systems over which the combatant commander has no technical control. CCDRs rely on JFHQ-DODIN to direct DODIN operations and DCO-IDM on these Service-maintained networks or other networks not technically controlled by the combatant commander.

JOINT CYBER CENTER

D-38. Many CCMDs centralize the staff actions for planning, integrating, synchronizing, monitoring, and assessing cyberspace operations within a joint cyber center. Personnel assigned to a joint cyber center are usually subject matter experts for OCO and DCO tactics, techniques, and procedures and serve as cyberspace advisors to the combatant commander. Each joint cyber center receives support from an assigned cyberspace operations-integrated planning element.

D-39. Army corps staff may interact with a joint cyber center or a cyberspace operations-integrated planning element when functioning as a JTF staff. In most other situations, Army corps staff will interact primarily with the cyberspace operations staff at a JTF or with the CEMA staff at a theater army. Army commanders and staff at echelons below corps will rarely interact with a joint cyberspace center or cyberspace operations-integrated planning element.

CYBERSPACE OPERATIONS-INTEGRATED PLANNING ELEMENT

D-40. The cyberspace operations-integrated planning element is a subordinate element of USCYBERCOM that integrates with a combatant commander's joint cyberspace center and staff to provide expertise to the CCMD and serve as a reachback to USCYBERCOM. Cyberspace operations-integrated planning elements are organized using personnel from USCYBERCOM, JFHQ-DODIN, and JFHQ-C, are operational control to the JFHQ-C that supports a particular CCMD, and are co-located with each CCMD for full integration into the joint cyberspace center or cyberspace staff. Cyberspace operations-integrated planning elements include cyberspace operations planners and other subject matter experts required to support the development of cyberspace operations related requirements in the AOR and to assist CCMD planners with coordinating, integrating, and deconflicting cyberspace operations.

D-41. The cyberspace operations-integrated planning element assists the joint cyberspace center in providing situational awareness and facilitating the acquisition of timely threat information related to cyberspace within the AOR. The cyberspace operations-integrated planning element assists with the cyberspace portion of the joint intelligence preparation of the operational environment, develops target system analysis products, and submits target nominations to the supported CCMD for candidate target list inclusion.

JOINT ELECTROMAGNETIC SPECTRUM OPERATIONS CELL

D-42. The JEMSOC includes EW and spectrum management experts who advise the combatant commander on tactics, techniques, and procedures for joint electromagnetic spectrum operations (JEMSO) throughout the AOR. The JEMSOC director is usually delegated electromagnetic spectrum coordinating authority from the combatant commander that allows the JEMSOC to provide unity of command in the EMS when the JTF operates within an AOR. Electromagnetic spectrum coordinating authority enables joint commanders with the authority to plan, coordinate, monitor, manage, assess, and prioritize execution of joint electromagnetic spectrum operations. The JEMSOC obtains EW assets by developing and disseminating electromagnetic spectrum operations orders to Service components operating within the AOR. Electromagnetic spectrum operations orders provide electromagnetic spectrum operations directives and includes the JEMSO plan.

D-43. The CCMD JEMSOC is responsible for all operational planning, execution, and assessment of JEMSO, unless the JTF JEMSOC has been established and delegated that responsibility. In this instance, the CCMD JEMSOC conducts theater-level planning, coordination, and guidance but delegates electromagnetic spectrum coordinating authority to the JTF JEMSOC to execute assigned missions in a designated joint operations area. The corps assigned as a JTF headquarters combines its spectrum management chief with its CEMA section to establish the Army component of its JEMSOC. Other Service components also establish EMSO cells to support the JTF headquarters.

D-44. The CCMD JEMSOC may limit electromagnetic spectrum coordinating authority delegated to the JTF JEMSOC and retain coordination and unifying command authorities. When delegated electromagnetic spectrum coordinating authority, the JTF executes EW missions through its assigned Service components. Each Service component will create a subordinate EMSO cell to establish command, staff, and technical channels between the JTF JEMSOC and their subordinate units. Figure D-2, page D-9, illustrates the notional EMSO organizational structure for command, staff, and technical channels. Command channels are direct chain-of-command transmission paths (ADP 6-0). Commanders and authorized staff officers use command channels for command-related activities. Staff officers use command channels for command-related activities. *Staff channels* are staff-to-staff transmission paths between headquarters and are used for control-related activities (ADP 6-0). Staff channels transmit planning information, status reports, controlling instructions, and other information to support mission command. *Technical channels* are the transmission paths between two technically similar units, offices, or staff sections that perform a technical function requiring special expertise or control the performance of technical functions (ADP 6-0). Technical channels are typically used to control performance of technical functions.

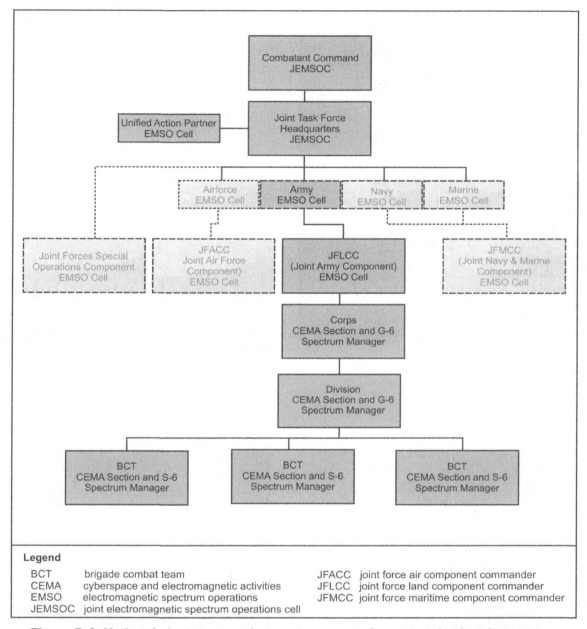

Figure D-2. National electromagnetic spectrum operations organizational structure.

D-45. A corps or division designated to command Army and Marine Corps forces in a joint operations area is called a joint force land component command. The joint force land component commander establishes its EMSO cell by integrating its spectrum management chief with its CEMA section. The JTF ensures JEMSO is conducted in the joint operations area in accordance with the combatant commander's established policies. For more information on JEMSO, refer to JP 3-85.

Other books we publish on Amazon.com

PODCAST: https://atp-3-2015-tank-platoon.castos.com

PODCAST: https://atp-3-218-infantry-platoon-and-squad.castos.com

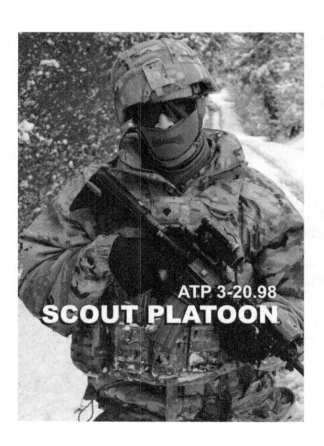

Appendix E

Request for Support

This appendix discusses how Army units request support for cyberspace operations and electromagnetic warfare during joint operations. Army forces may require offensive cyberspace operations support for identified targets that require engagement using cyberspace attacks. Defensive cyberspace operations support may be necessary when an identified threat in friendly cyberspace is beyond the scope of cyberspace security. Electromagnetic warfare support may be required when an Army unit needs augmentation or when their electromagnetic warfare capabilities or authorities cannot fulfill the requirements to support operations or the commander's intent.

SECTION I – REQUESTING CYBERSPACE AND ELECTROMAGNETIC WARFARE SUPPORT

E-1. This section describes procedures to request DCO-IDM, OCO, and DCO-RA support at corps and below. It also discusses how Army units request non-organic EW support as an augmentation to fulfill targeting gaps.

OVERVIEW OF REQUEST FOR SUPPORT

E-2. In conjunction with the necessary legal and operational authorities, commanders select organic EW capabilities to create desired effects on targets identified for EAs. If a unit's organic EW capabilities do not fulfill the targeting requirements to support the commander's intent, or if the commander does not have the authority to employ a particular EW capability, the CEMA section requests support from the next higher echelon. To request EA that will be administered by aircraft, the CEMA section uses the Joint Tactical Air Strike Request and the support request tool.

E-3. As requests pass from echelon to echelon, each echelon processes the Joint Tactical Air Strike Request to assess their ability to provide the support that meets the requesting unit's requirements. The requirement elevates either until it reaches an echelon that can support the requesting unit or until the highest echelon denies the request. Supporting a requesting unit may not be possible due to prioritization, timing, capabilities, authorization, or conflict with other EW capability requirements. Commanders ultimately have the responsibility for denying resource requests and may delegate that authority to their staff. The joint force commander may refuse a request for joint air resources, but not the joint force air component commander.

E-4. Corps and below units do not have organic cyberspace capabilities to conduct DCO-IDM, DCO-RA, or OCO missions. The G-3 or S-3 requests support through higher headquarters. The G-6 or S-6 and the CEMA section coordinate to request DCO-IDM after determining that a threat in friendly cyberspace is beyond the scope of cyberspace security. DCO-IDM is an enabler for DCO-RA. Cyber mission forces performing DCO-IDM request DCO-RA upon deciding that a cyberspace threat requires a defensive attack beyond friendly cyberspace. OCO is used to create desired effects on targets identified for cyberspace attacks on the integrated target list. DCO-RA and OCO are similar except that DCO-RA is only used to deter a threat, whereas OCO is used to project power.

REQUESTING OFFENSIVE CYBERSPACE OPERATIONS SUPPORT

E-5. For OCO missions, the CEMA working group identifies targets that have met the established targeting selection standards during the targeting process (see Chapter 4) and aligned with the commanders' targeting guidance. Once approved, the fires support element adds these targets to the unit's high payoff target list with all other identified non-cyberspace related targets. The CEMA working group will also make recommendations to the no-strike list and restricted target list that supports the commanders targeting guidance.

E-6.   Combat mission teams provide OCO capabilities to corps and below units per request through the RFS process. Upon the commander's approval, the CEMA section submits an RFS along with the high payoff target list, no-strike list, and restricted target list, to higher headquarters through the joint force land component command, to the JTF headquarters as nominations for the joint targeting cycle and joint no-strike list or restricted target list. Targets that require OCO-related tasks should include such data as known IP addresses, if possible, known physical locations, and any known cyber-personas associated with the target.

E-7.   Once the JTF headquarters approves the OCO related targets identified in the corps' high payoff target list, they will add them to the joint targeting cycle. The JTF headquarters then continues the RFS process to receive OCO support from JFHQ-C (See figure E-1 on page E-3).

Note. USCYBERCOM does not accept the cyber effects request format (CERF). The staff uses a RFS to request OCO support in a joint environment. JTF headquarters and their subordinate units must become familiar with the RFS or any other standardized requesting format established by USCYBERCOM and the CCMD before requesting support. The joint force land component command, converts all CERFs received from Army forces to RFS formats before forwarding to the JTF headquarters.

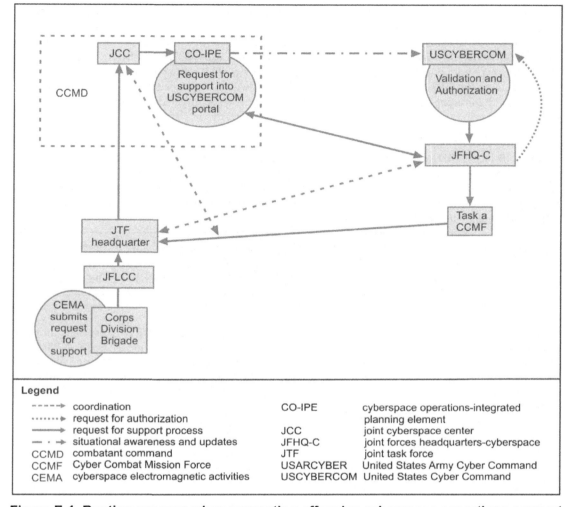

Figure E-1. Routing process when requesting offensive cyberspace operations support

REQUESTING DEFENSIVE CYBERSPACE OPERATIONS SUPPORT

E-8.   Corps and below units do not have organic DCO-IDM capabilities and must request for DCO-IDM-related tasks through the RFS process. DCO-IDM support is necessary for threats on the DODIN-A beyond the scope or abilities of organic cyberspace forces conducting cyberspace security. Units request DCO-IDM as a reactive measure to defend against a cyberspace threat. The G-6 or S-6 coordinates with the G-3 or S-3 to develop an RFS requesting DCO-IDM support.

E-9.   Upon commander's approval, the RFS is submitted, validated, and channeled to higher headquarters, through the joint force land component command, to JTF headquarters until it reaches the CCMD's joint cyberspace center. The requesting unit additionally informs a cybersecurity service provider (Defense Information Systems Agency or NETCOM) of the cyberspace threat. The JTF headquarters routes the RFS; the cybersecurity service provider also notifies JFHQ-DODIN of the identified cyberspace threat. The CCMD has organic CCMD CPTs that conduct DCO-IDM in friendly cyberspace. CCDRs have directive authority for cyberspace operations that authorizes DCO-IDM missions within their assigned AOR without requesting authorization from USCYBERCOM.

E-10. The CCMD CPTs primary focus is employing DCO-IDM throughout the AOR and may be unavailable to provide support to requesting corps and below units. If the CCMD CPTs are unavailable, the joint cyberspace center forwards the RFS through the cyberspace operations-integrated planning element to the

JFHQ-DODIN through the USCYBERCOM portal. The cyberspace operations-integrated planning element provides situational awareness of all DCO-IDM missions conducted in the AOR to USCYBERCOM.

Note. When a cybersecurity service provider becomes aware of a threat on the DODIN, it forwards the information to JFHQ-DODIN. The JFHQ-DODIN uses the notice from the cybersecurity service provider to begin the process of employing a CPT (either DODIN or Service) before receiving the RFS through the routing channels. However, the requesting unit is still responsible for both initiating the RFS process and informing a cybersecurity service provider.

E-11. JFHQ-DODIN has directive authority for cyberspace operations to conduct DCO-IDM globally on the DODIN. JFHQ-DODIN provides situational awareness to USCYBERCOM regarding all DCO-IDM missions. JFHQ-DODIN also have tactical control of all Service cyberspace component commands for DODIN operations and DCO-IDM only. JFHQ-DODIN has DODIN CPTs that conduct DCO-IDM; however, their primary focus is generally on monitoring and implementing proactive DCO-IDM to mitigate cyberspace threats on the DODIN globally.

Note. Initiating DCO-IDM to respond to a cyberspace threat proactively uses a top-down approach. Proactive DCO-IDM occurs when JFHQ-DODIN identifies a cyberspace threat on the DODIN, before receiving an RFS or being informed by a cybersecurity service provider, and proactively deploy a CPT (either DODIN or Service) to mitigate the cyberspace threat.

E-12. If the DODIN CPTs are unavailable to satisfy the RFS, JFHQ-DODIN oversees a joint approval process to task one of the Service cyberspace component commands to provide a Service CPT to conduct DCO-IDM in support of the unit's request. The assigned CPT may perform DCO-IDM remotely or collocate with the JTF headquarters or requesting unit. When collocated with the unit, the CPT is still under the command of its organic unit. Figure E-2, page E-5, illustrates the routing process for requesting DCO-IDM support for corps and below.

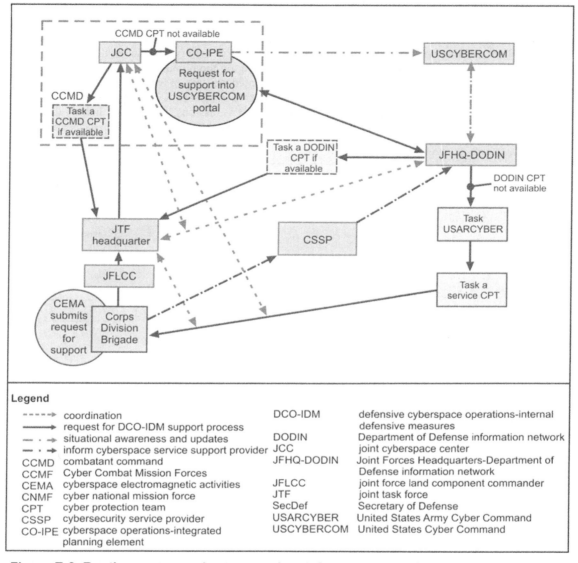

Figure E-2. Routing process when requesting defensive cyberspace operations-internal defensive measures support

DEFENSIVE CYBERSPACE OPERATIONS SUPPORT FOR NON-DEPARTMENT OF DEFENSE FRIENDLY CYBERSPACE

E-13. An RFS requesting assistance for a threat detected on a critical network located in non-DODIN friendly cyberspace is sent to the CNMF-HQs to employ a national CPT to conduct DCO-IDM. National CPTs only conduct DCO-IDM in non-DODIN friendly cyberspace. Non-DODIN friendly cyberspace includes critical networks in which mission partners perform cyberspace operations and areas of cyberspace where the Secretary of Defense orders the DOD to protect. CNMF-HQ has directive authority for cyberspace operations that allows it to conduct DCO-IDM in non-DODIN friendly cyberspace without authorization from USCYBERCOM. However, CNMF-HQ is responsible for ensuring USCYBERCOM maintains situational awareness on all DCO-IDM missions.

DEFENSIVE CYBERSPACE OPERATIONS-RESPONSE ACTIONS SUPPORT

E-14. CNMFs, consisting of national mission teams and NSTs assigned to CNMF-HQ, conduct DCO-RA missions upon requests from CPTs (at any echelon) when a more progressive defensive approach goes outside of the DODIN and into neutral and enemy cyberspace. DCO-RA may rise to the level of force resulting in physical damage or destruction of enemy systems depending on the broader operational context. DCO-RA tactics have many similarities to OCO, requiring coordinated military orders and careful consideration of scope, rules of engagement, and measurable objectives. For these reasons, CNMF-HQ must attain validation and authorization from USCYBERCOM to conduct DCO-RA missions. Figure E-3, below, illustrates the routing process for requesting DCO-IDM support for non-DODIN friendly cyberspace and DCO-RA support.

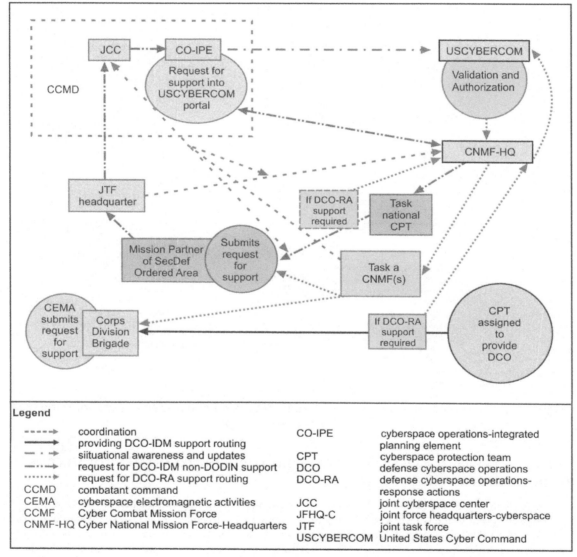

Figure E-3. Routing process for defensive cyberspace operations-internal defensive measures (non-Department of Defense information network) and defensive cyberspace operations-response actions support

REQUESTING CYBERSPACE EFFECTS (ECHELON CORPS AND BELOW)

E-15. CERF is the format corps and below units use to request cyberspace support. Support in response to a CERF may come from joint cyberspace forces such as the combat mission teams, from other joint or Service capabilities, or Service-retained cyberspace forces.

EFFECTS APPROVAL AT ECHELONS CORPS AND BELOW

E-16. During the operations process at echelons corps and below, the commander and staff identify the effects desired in and through cyberspace to support operations against specific targets. If the requesting and higher echelons determine that a current capability is insufficient, the commander and staff approve and processes the CERF. The routing process continues to each echelon until the CERF reaches the joint force land component command it is converted to an RFS, and forwarded to the JTF headquarters. The CERF approval process at echelons corps and below follow the below steps—

- Identify targets of cyberspace effects.
- Verify if organic capabilities can create desired effects.
- Approve target for cyberspace effects.
- Forward to next higher Army echelon for deconfliction and synchronization.
- Verify if other organic capabilities can create desired effects if organic cyberspace capabilities do not exist.
- If current capabilities fulfill the requirement, synchronize operations.
- If current capabilities do not fulfill the requirement, approve target for cyberspace effects.
- Forward to next higher Army echelon for approval until CERF enters the joint process.
- Synchronize operation with cyberspace effect (if possible).

Note. The joint force land component command may require the requesting corps to convert the CERF to an RFS format before submitting it into the joint process.

EFFECTS APPROVAL AT ECHELONS ABOVE CORPS

E-17. Cyberspace operations provide a means by which Army forces can achieve periods or instances of cyberspace superiority to create effects to support the commander's objectives. Cyberspace attack capabilities are tailored to create specific effects and must be planned, prepared, and executed using existing processes and procedures. Commander and staff at all echelons apply additional measures for determining where, when, and how to use cyberspace effects.

E-18. Commanders and staff at each echelon will coordinate and collaborate regardless of whether the cyberspace operation is directed from higher headquarters or requested from subordinate units. The Army intelligence process, informed by the joint intelligence process, provides the necessary analysis and products from which targets are vetted and validated, and aim points are derived. As a result of the IPB process, and in collaboration with the joint intelligence preparation of the operational environment process, intelligence personnel develop network topologies for enemy, adversary, and host nation technical networks.

E-19. Targets determined during the planning process are described broadly as physical and logical entities in cyberspace consisting of one or more networked devices used by enemy and adversary actors. The G-2 may label these targets as named areas of interest and target areas of interest. Additionally, an analysis of friendly force networks will inform the development of critical information and provide a basis for establishing key terrain in cyberspace. Critical network nodes are key terrain in cyberspace. They include those physical and logical entities in friendly force technical networks of such extraordinary importance that any disruption in their operation would have debilitating effects on accomplishing the mission.

E-20. As part of CEMA, the staff will perform a key role in target network node analysis. While determining cyberspace attack effect-types for targets and defensive measures for critical network nodes, the CEMA section will prepare, submit, and track the CERF. This request will elevate above the corps echelon and integrate into the joint targeting cycle for follow-on processing and approval.

CYBER EFFECTS REQUEST FORMAT PREPARATION

E-21. Although the requesting unit may not have the specific target network topology information, it should provide current target information. The approval process for cyberspace effects may take longer than other targeting capabilities. Each of the three sections in the cyber effects request are described below in bullet format. The requesting unit provides all information from the bullet lists below to higher headquarters through the CEMA working group or other designated targeting processes.

CYBER EFFECTS REQUEST FORMAT SECTION 1 REQUESTING UNIT INFORMATION

E-22. Section 1 of the CERF requests the following unit information—

- **Supported Major Command.** Enter the major command authorized to validate and prioritize the CERF. For Army units at corps level and below, this entry will commonly include the geographic or functional combatant command.
- **Date.** Enter the date the requesting unit submitted the CERF to higher headquarters.
- **Time Sent.** Enter the time the requesting united submitted the CERF to higher headquarters.
- **Requesting Unit.** Enter the name of the requesting unit.
- **By.** Enter the rank, last, and the first name of the requesting unit's point of contact that time-stamped and processed the CERF.
- **Point of Contact.** Enter the rank, last, and the first name of the requesting unit's point of contact. Also, enter the phone number and e-mail.
- **Classification.** Enter the overall classification of the document. Ensure classification markings are applied to each section and supporting documentation.

CYBER EFFECTS REQUEST FORMAT SECTION 2 SUPPORTED OPERATION INFORMATION

E-23. Section 2 of the CERF requests the following supported operation information—

- **Supported OPLAN/CONPLAN/Order.** Describe key details within the plan that the requested cyberspace attack will support.
- **Supported Mission Statement.** Describe the unit's essential task(s) and the purpose that the requested effect(s) will support.
- **Supported Commander's Intent.** Describe key information within the commander's intent that the requested effect(s) will support.
- **Supported Commander's End State.** Describe key information within the commander's end state that the requested effect(s) will support.
- **Supported Concept of Operations.** Describe key information within the concept of operations that the requested effect(s) will support.
- **Supported Objective (strategic, operational, and tactical).** Describe the supported objective(s) that the requested effect(s) will directly support.
- **Supported Tactical Objective/Task.** Describe the tactical objectives and tasks that the requested effect(s) will directly or indirectly support.

CYBER EFFECTS REQUEST FORMAT SECTION 3 COMPUTER NETWORK OPERATIONS

E-24. Section 3 of the CERF requests the following computer network operations and specific information—

- **Type of Target.**
  - Indicate *scheduled* if specific dates, times, and or supporting conditions are known.
  - Indicate *on-call* if trigger events or supporting conditions are known.
- **Target Priority.**

- ▪ Indicate *emergency* if the target requires immediate action. Indicate *priority* if the target requires a degree of urgency.
- ▪ Indicate *routine* if the target does not require immediate action or a degree of urgency beyond standard processing.
- **Target Name**. Enter the name of the target as codified in the Modernized Integrated Database.
- **Target Location**.
  - ▪ Provide the target location
  - ▪ Disregard if the request is for DCO-IDM.
- **Target Description**.
  - ▪ Provide the target description.
  - ▪ Describe the network node(s) wherein specific activities are to support DCO-IDM.
- **Desired Effect**.
  - ▪ Enter deny, degrade, disrupt, destroy, or manipulate for OCO.
  - ▪ Provide timing as *less than 96 hours*, *96 hours to 90 days*, or *greater than 90 days*.
- **Target Function**. Enter target(s) primary function and additional functions if known.
- **Target Significance**. Describe why the target(s) is important to the enemy's or adversary's target system(s) or value in addition to its functions and expectations.
- **Target Details**. Describe additional information about the target(s) if known. This information should include any relevant device information such as type, number of users; activity; friendly actors in the area of operations; and surrounding/adjacent/parallel devices.
- **Concept of Cyberspace Operations**.
  - ▪ Describe how the requested effect(s) would contribute to the commander's objectives and overall operations concept.
  - ▪ Include the task, purpose, method, and end state.
  - ▪ Describe the intelligence collection plan and specific assessment plan if known.
  - ▪ Provide a reference to key directives and orders.
- **Target Expectation Statement**. According to CJCSI 3370.01C, Enclosure D describes how the requested effect(s) will impact the target system(s). This description must address the following questions.
  - ▪ How will the target system be affected if the target's function is neutralized, delayed, disrupted, or degraded? (Two examples are operational impact and psychological impact.)
  - ▪ What is the estimated degree of impact on the target system(s)?
  - ▪ What is the functional recuperation time estimated for the target system(s) if the target's function is neutralized, delayed, disrupted, or degraded?
  - ▪ What distinct short-term or long-term military or political advantage/disadvantage do we expect if the target's function is neutralized, delayed, disrupted, or degraded?
  - ▪ What is the expected enemy or adversary reaction to affecting the target's function?

SECTION II – REQUESTING AIRBORNE SUPPORT

E-25. Typically, Army units at corps and below have the organic capabilities to conduct EW within their assigned AO. The joint force commander typically delegates electromagnetic attack control authority to subordinate commanders conducting EW missions within their assigned AO. Commanders must ensure EW has been integrated and synchronized across the staff and according to the higher commander's guidance parameters.

E-26. Units may require an EW capability not organically available or additional EW assets to meet requirements identified during the targeting cycle or target development process. The commander and the CEWO request augmentation through a higher, adjacent, or lower headquarters to meet requirements. This section describes procedures for requesting airborne cyberspace and EA support. It also discusses the use of the five-line electromagnetic attack request for immediate airborne EA.

AIRBORNE ELECTROMAGNETIC ATTACK SUPPORT

E-27. In a joint environment, Army units can request an airborne cyberspace attack, EA or ES. Targeting using airborne assets for cyberspace and EA can be used for both deliberate and dynamic targets. In this instance, the unit submits DD Form 1972 (Joint Tactical Air Strike Request), accompanied by an airborne cyberspace attack, electromagnetic attack, or electromagnetic support request tool. Each of these requests have unique information requirements and request flows. The requesting unit's fires support element adds the target to its target nomination list. The target is also added to the joint integrated prioritized target list at the JTF headquarters and forwarded to the joint force air component command with its assigned DD Form 1972 (Joint Tactical Air Strike Request) number (see ATP 3-09.32). Once the joint force air component command approves the Joint Tactical Air Strike Request, the request is forwarded to the air operations center to execute the attack.

E-28. Table E-1, below, is an example of the request tool used to request an airborne EA or ES and accompanies a DD Form 1972 (Joint Tactical Air Strike Request) (see page E-12).

Table E-1. Airborne cyberspace attack, electromagnetic attack, or electromagnetic support request tool

| Nonkinetic Effect Discipline (Space, Airborne Electro-magnetic Attack, Information Operations, or Cyber) | Applicable phase or Find, Fix Track, Target, Engage, Assess | Nonkinetic Effect | Risk | | | Aproval Timeline (idea to Approved Execution Order) | Employment Timeline (initial Access to Effect Ready to Fire) | Authority Level (for use in Area of Responsibility) | Execution Authority (Tactical Employment) |
			Technical Gain/ Loss	Intel Gain/ Loss	Commander's Acceptable Level or Risk				
....	....	....	....	....	....	....	....	....	....
....	....	....	....	....	....	....	....	....	....
Airborne EA	Target	Jam	Gain	Gain	Acceptable	180 mins	180 mins	Local	Local
....	....	....	....	....	....	....	....	....	....
....	....	....	....	....	....	....	....	....	....

Figure E-4, below, illustrates a DD Form 1972 (Joint Tactical Air Strike Request).

JOINT TACTICAL AIR STRIKE REQUEST	See Joint Pub 3-09.3 for preparation instructions.

SECTION I - MISSION REQUEST — DATE

1. UNIT CALLED: Chieftan — THIS IS: Gator 01 — REQUEST NUMBER: IA9501-A — SENT: TIME 1615 BY Maj Smith

2. PREPLANNED: A PRECEDENCE 4 — B PRIORITY II — IMMEDIATE: C PRIORITY — RECEIVED: TIME 1615 BY SrA Ford

3. TARGET IS/NUMBER OF:
A PERS IN OPEN 20-30 — B PERS DUG IN — C WPNS/MG/RR/AT — D MORTARS, ARTY
E AAA ADA — F RKTS MISSILE — G ARMOR 3xBTR in line — H VEHICLES 4 Stationary
I BLDGS 2 — J BRIDGES — K PILLBOX, BUNKERS — L SUPPLIES, EQUIP
M CENTER (CP, COM) — N AREA — O ROUTE — P MOVING N E S W
Q REMARKS

4. TARGET LOCATION IS:
A 11SUG8005 (COORDINATES) — B — C — D — CHECKED BY SSgt Intel
E TGT ELEV 10 — F SHEET NO. 2875 II — G SERIES V795S — H CHART NO.

5. TARGET TIME/DATE: A ASAP — B NLT 1600 — C AT — D TO

6. DESIRED ORD/RESULTS: A ORDNANCE LGB/Guns — B DESTROY — C NEUTRALIZE X — D HARASS/INTERDICT

7. FINAL CONTROL: A FAC/RABFAC II — B CALL SIGN GATOR 20 — C FREQ Orange 17 — D CONT PT JACKS

8. REMARKS

SECTION II - COORDINATION

9. NSFS 4XTLAM FLA 1 SS — 10. ARTY — 11. AIO/G-2/G-3

12. REQUEST: X APPROVED / DISAPPROVED — 13. BY Maj Hughes — 14. REASON FOR DISAPPROVAL

15. RESTRICTIVE FIRE/AIR PLAN: A IS NOT IN EFFECT — B NUMBER — 16. IS IN EFFECT: A (FROM TIME) — B (TO TIME)

17. LOCATION: A (FROM COORDINATES) — B (TO COORDINATES) — 18. WIDTH (METERS) — 19. ALTITUDE/VERTEX: A (MAXIMUM/VERTEX) — B (MINIMUM)

SECTION III - MISSION DATA

20. MISSION NUMBER	21. CALL SIGN	22. NO. AND TYPE AIRCRAFT	23. ORDNANCE
3021/3022	Razor 51/52 Venom 16-17	(2) AV-8B (2) AH-1Z	SCL 1/3
24. EST/ACT TAKEOFF 1424	25. EST TOT 1438	26. CONT PT (COORDS) Breaker	27. INITIAL CONTACT
28. FAC/FAC(A)/TAC(A) CALL SIGN/FREQ	29. AIRSPACE COORDINATION AREA	30. TGT DESCRIPTION	*31. TGT COORD/ELEV

32. BATTLE DAMAGE ASSESSMENT (BDA) REPORT (USMTF INFLTREP)
LINE 1/CALL SIGN Razor 51/52 — LINE 4/LOCATION 18SUG8005
LINE 2/MSN NUMBER 3021/3022 — LINE 5/TOT 1454
LINE 3/REQ NUMBER 1A9501-A — LINE 6/RESULTS Neutralize/Destory
REMARKS — *TRANSMIT AS APPROPRIATE

DD FORM 1972, MAY 2019 — PREVIOUS EDITION MAY BE USED. — Adobe Professional 7.0

Figure E-4. Joint tactical airstrike request form.

E-29. The air operations center is responsible for overseeing the employment of airborne EA assets on the air tasking order. Airborne EA assets provide friendly forces with options to mitigate threats and give commanders options for targeting. Multiple configurations and capabilities exist for airborne EA to mitigate targets in land, sea, and air domains. See ATP 3-60.1 for a list of available airborne EA capabilities and configurations. The air operations center is the primary contact to determine in-flight capability for targeting.

ELECTROMAGNETIC ATTACK REQUEST

E-30. *Dynamic targeting* is targeting that prosecutes targets identified too late or not selected for action in time to be included in deliberate targeting. Dynamic targeting is normally employed in current operations planning because the nature and timeframe associated with current operations typically requires more immediate responsiveness than is achieved in deliberate targeting (JP 3-60). Dynamic targeting is used for targets of opportunity that includes unscheduled targets and unanticipated targets. When immediate airborne EA is required for deliberate targeting, for example, when a ground maneuver unit requires jamming enemy communications before engagement, a unit can request support using an EA request. Units also submit an EA request for EA support when a mission cannot pre-plan due to some operations' immediate nature. The EA request prepares the aircrew providing EA support (see ATP 3-09.32). The JTF headquarters, the joint force land component command, the joint force air component command, and the air operations center must collaboratively plan airborne EA before an operation. This planning and coordination provides the joint force air component command the necessary time to identify and prepare an electronic combat squadron that will remain on standby throughout the mission. Figure E-5 on page E-13 depicts an EA request.

Electromagnetic Attack Request

Do not transmit line numbers. Units of measure are standard unless briefed.

Lines 1,2 and 4 are mandatory readback (*). Jam Control Authority (JTAC) may request additional readback.

JCA; "_____ Foxfire 06 _____. this is _____ Forward 09 _____,"
(aircraft call sign)   (JTAC call sign)

1. Target/ or Effect Description:"_____ Disrupt _____,"

    a. Rapper or Target Name   radio transmitter
    b. Frequency (if known)   107.1 MHZ
    c. Modulation   FM

2. Target Location; "_____ N 46° 41 33. 8 W 120° 947.2322" _____,"
    (latitude and longitude or MGRS)

3. Remarks:" _____ no current remarks or special instructions _____,"

Legend

JTAC   joint terminal attack controller   N North
MGRS military grid reference system   W West

Figure E-5. Electromagnetic attack request.

Note. The electromagnetic attack request is the common format for requesting airborne EA support. The CAOC Non-Kinetic Operations Center may require the use of a different requesting procedure for immediate EA support. The JTF headquarters and its subordinate units must become familiar with the standardized EA requesting format established by the CAOC Non-Kinetic Operations Center or the CCMD before requesting EA support. Additionally, a tactical air control party or joint terminal attack controller may handle electromagnetic attack requests because of its uniqueness and necessity for the particular tactical experience required.

Other books we publish on Amazon.com

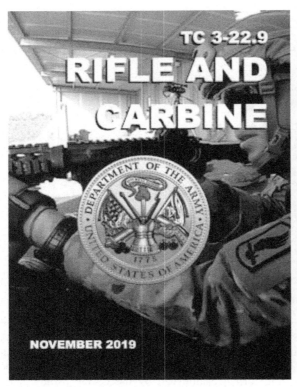

TC 3-22.9
RIFLE AND CARBINE

NOVEMBER 2019

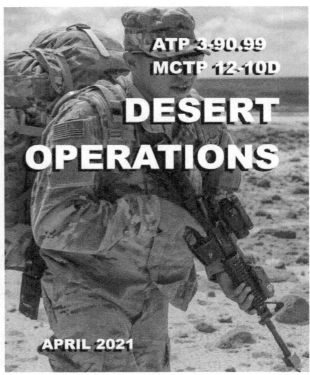

ATP 3-90.99
MCTP 12-10D
DESERT OPERATIONS

APRIL 2021

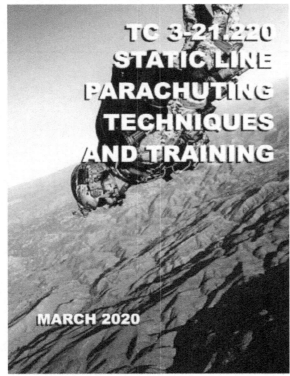

TC 3-21.220
STATIC LINE PARACHUTING TECHNIQUES AND TRAINING

MARCH 2020

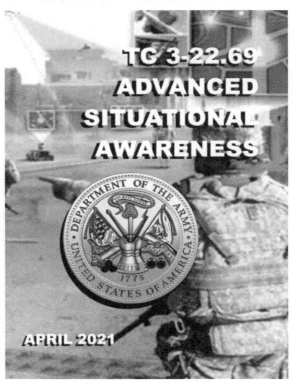

TC 3-22.69
ADVANCED SITUATIONAL AWARENESS

APRIL 2021

Includes info on REAL-TIME ELECTRONIC SPECTRUM SITUATIONAL AWARENESS

Appendix F
Electromagnetic Warfare Reprogramming

This appendix provides general procedures in conducting electromagnetic warfare reprogramming, divided into four phases. It will also describe the three major categories of electromagnetic warfare reprogramming and associated actions. It will also discuss the joint coordination of electromagnetic warfare reprogramming.

PURPOSE OF ELECTROMAGNETIC REPROGRAMMING

F-1.   The purpose of EW reprogramming is to maintain or enhance the effectiveness of EW and TSS equipment. EW reprogramming includes changes to self-defense systems, offensive weapons systems, and intelligence collection systems. Each Army unit is responsible for reprogramming of EW and TSS equipment using an established EW reprogramming support program.

F-2.   Units from all Service components that identify threat signature changes report those changes through higher headquarters to the CCMD of the AOR in which they are conducting operations. The Service intelligence production center [National Ground Intelligence Center for the Army]; and Service equipment support for effected EW and TSS equipment.

F-3.   The CCMD ensures promulgating the threat signature changes worldwide and to Service components operating through the AOR using joint coordination electromagnetic warfare reprogramming policies and procedures developed by the Joint Staff. The Intelligence Production Center collects the data to process and analyze to identify and understand the threat signature change. Service equipment support conducts flagging activities while analyzing EW and TSS equipment for compatibility and system impact assessment.

Note. EW reprogramming is only required for EW and targeting sensing software that operate using downloads of threat signatures. With these systems, EW reprogramming occurs when threat signatures have changed. Dynamic EW capabilities do not require downloads of threat signatures and thus do not require EW reprogramming.

CATEGORIES OF ELECTROMAGNETIC WARFARE REPROGRAMMING

F-4.   Several types of changes constitute EW reprogramming. These changes fall into three major categories of EW reprogramming. They are –

- **Tactics.** Include changes in procedures, equipment, settings, or EW systems mission-planning data. These changes are usually conducted at the Service level and implemented at the unit level using organic personnel and equipment.
- **Software.** Include changes to the programming of computer-based EW and target sensing software. This type of change requires software vendors to alter programmed look-up tables, threat libraries, or signal sorting routines.
- **Hardware.** Hardware changes or long-term system development are necessary due to tactics and software changes installed to resolve deficiencies. These changes usually occur tactical, and software changes are of such complexity that it requires hardware modifications or upgrades.

ELECTROMAGNETIC WARFARE REPROGRAMMING ACTIONS

F-5.   During a crisis or enemy EA, EW reprogramming provides commanders with a timely capability to respond to threat systems changes and correct EW and targeting sensing systems. Through EW reprogramming, commanders can also adjust EW, TSS deficiencies and tailor EW and TSS to meet unique mission requirements. EW reprogramming enables this capability using three different EW reprogramming actions, either individually or simultaneously. These reprogramming actions are–

- **Threat changes.** Any changes in the operation or electromagnetic signature of a threat system. The design of EW reprogramming is to respond to threat changes that affect EW's combat effectiveness and TSS.
- **Geographic tailoring.** The reprogramming of EW and targeting sensing systems for operations in a specific area or region of the world. Geographic tailoring reduces the number of system memory threats, decreasing systems processing time, and reducing error displays.
- **Mission tailoring.** The reprogramming of EW and targeting sensing systems for the mission of the host platform. Mission tailoring may improve system response to the priority threat(s) identified by the host platform.

GENERAL ELECTROMAGNETIC WARFARE REPROGRAMMING PROCESS

F-6.   There are four phases to the EW reprogramming process. Units can further refine the last three phases of the EW reprogramming process to meet their unique requirements. The four phases of the EW reprogramming process are—

- Determine the threat.
- Determine the response.
- Create a change.
- Implement the change.

Determine the Threat

F-7.   When determining the threat, units develop and maintain an accurate description of the EMOE, specifically threat systems and tactics. Document submitted IRs to maintain an accurate description of the EMOE at all times. IRs are important since EW and TSS equipment are each programmed to identify and respond to a particular threat or target signature data. An accurate description of the EMOE requires the fusion of known electromagnetic data with the collection, analysis, and validation of threat signature changes divided into three steps:

- **Collect data.** Threat signature data collection is the collection of threat system parametric information and is the responsibility of the G-2 or S-2. The collection of signature data may be a matter of routine intelligence collection against targeted systems. Other data collection may occur because of urgent intelligence production requests. Regardless of the purpose of collection, signature data disseminates through the intelligence channels to the National Ground Intelligence Center and the EW and TSS Service equipment support channels for analysis and flagging activities.
- **Identify changes.** EW and TSS Service equipment support analyzes the collected data for compatibility. Incompatible data is *flagged* for further analysis and system impact assessment. The National Ground Intelligence Center uses the collected data for processing and analysis to identify threat signature changes in the EMOE. Identified changes are further analyzed.
- **Validate changes.** Once an identified signature change is correlated to a threat system and analyzed, it is further analyzed to validate an actual system capability change or determine it as a probable malfunction. Information on threat system engineering and tactical employment are critical during this step. The National Ground Intelligence Center or the Defense Intelligence Agency(s) typically provide technical analysis and validation of threat changes. At the joint level, the CCMD must provide the identification, technical description, and analysis of threat change validation messages expeditiously to component commands and Service reprogramming centers [Army Reprogramming Analysis Team for the Army].

Determine the Response

F-8.   Service reprogramming centers assess validated threat change information for its impact on friendly EW and TSS equipment. A decision to initiate a reprogramming change is determined. The equipment may fail to provide appropriate indications and warnings or countermeasures in response to a threat change. In this instance, the Service reprogramming center determines if the requirement to correct the deficiency is either by changing tactics, software, or hardware.

F-9.   Service equipment support generates a system impact message that informs CCMDs and component commands of the threat change's operational impact on EW and TSS equipment performance. The CCMDs forward the system impact message through the JTF headquarters to subordinate units. The system impact message often includes recommendations to respond to each identified threat change appropriately; however, each unit is ultimately responsible for determining the appropriate response action to a validated threat change.

Create the Change

F-10.   The unit develops tactics, software, or hardware changes to regain or improve equipment performance and combat effectiveness. The first option to consider when creating a change is in using tactics to avoid the threat. Tactical change is typically the first option because software and hardware changes require time that may not be readily available. Units are ultimately responsible for initiating tactical change as the initial change to continue operations until software and hardware changes are made available by the Service equipment support.

F-11.   A combination of changes (such as tactics and software) often provides an immediate and long-term fix to equipment deficiencies. Software and hardware changes require assistance from the EW and TSS Service equipment support. Service equipment support conducts reprogramming support activities to verify equipment combat effectiveness through modeling and simulation, bench tests, or test range employments simulating operational conditions.

Implement the Change

F-12.   Implementation of the change ensures units regain or attain enhanced combat effectiveness by tactics, software, or hardware change(s). CCMDs ensure subordinate units successfully incorporate tactics changes into mission pre-briefs. Service equipment support collaborates with other Services to install electronic and mechanical software and hardware changes to host EW and TSS equipment.

Other books we publish on Amazon.com

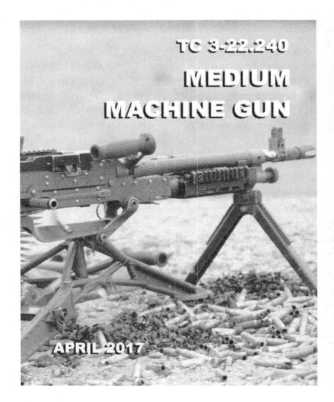

TC 3-22.240
MEDIUM MACHINE GUN
APRIL 2017

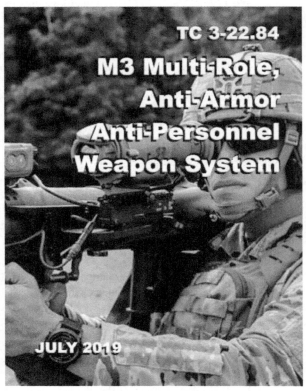

TC 3-22.84
M3 Multi-Role, Anti-Armor Anti-Personnel Weapon System
JULY 2019

INTEGRATED WEAPONS TRAINING STRATEGY (IWTS)

TC 3-22.249
LIGHT MACHINE GUN M249 Series
MAY 2017

Appendix G

Training

Training prepares Soldiers to execute missions that shape operational environment, prevent conflict, and conduct large-scale combat operations against peer threats. Army forces must be organized, trained, and equipped to meet worldwide challenges. The Army plans and executes tough, realistic training that includes unit training that occurs continuously while at home station, at a combat training center, and during deployments.

OVERVIEW OF TRAINING

G-1. Commanders ensure Soldiers and units train under challenging and realistic conditions that closely replicate an OE while incorporating the Army principles of training:
- Train as you fight.
- Train to standard.
- Train to sustain.
- Train to maintain.

G-2. Individual training occurs in all three training domains: institutional, operational, and self-development. Institutional training includes initial and ongoing individual training aligned with each cyberspace and EW professional's individual development plan. Additionally, Soldiers conduct individual and collective training during home-station and combat training to stay abreast of the continually advancing techniques, technologies, and trends that occur in cyberspace and the EMS.

INSTITUTIONAL TRAINING

G-3. Commissioned officers, warrant officers, and enlisted Soldiers seeking a career in cyberspace operations and EW benefit from intensive institutional training before forwarding to their first assigned unit. Institutional training will continue throughout these Soldiers' careers. Cyber Common Technical College and Electronic Warfare College resides at the United States Army Cyber Center of Excellence. These colleges provide institutional training to active Army, United States Army Reserve, and Army National Guard cyberspace and EW Soldiers with a level of understanding in cyberspace operations, electromagnetic warfare, and associated doctrine. Cyber Soldiers learn how to combine Army operations, intelligence, and small unit tactics with foundational skills in cyberspace offensive and defensive tasks. EW Soldiers learn Army operations and small unit tactics with foundational skills in EA, ES, and EP tasks. Events conducted during institutional training ensure cyberspace operations and EW Soldiers become proficient in their respective career fields and include such training events as—
- Classroom training consisting of instruction from civilian and military institutional instructors.
- Training lanes.
- Capstone training events.

HOME-STATION TRAINING

G-4. The CEWO is responsible for coordinating with each subordinate staff to conceive and implement an annual home-station training plan. The CEWO aligns the home-station training plan with the unit's mission essential task list consisting of essential individual and collective tasks that Soldiers must accomplish. The CEWO aligns home-station training with how the unit will operate during evaluations at a combat training center. The home-station training plan includes subject matter that ensures the unit's cyberspace operations and EW professionals remain proficient in their respective career fields and can consist of such training events as—

- Classroom training and instruction from mobile training team(s) (MTT).
- Training lanes.
- Field training exercises.

G-5. At a minimum, classroom training for cyberspace operations Soldiers should include DCO-IDM related instructions including—

- Securing Windows operating systems.
- Computer forensic investigation.
- Incident response.
- Intrusion detection in-depth.
- Hacker techniques.
- Exploits and incident mitigation and prevention.
- Network penetration testing.
- Ethical hacking.
- Auditing networks, perimeters, and information technology systems.

G-6. At a minimum, classroom training for EW Soldiers should include—

- General mathematic and algebraic concepts.
- Radio frequency fundamentals and calculations.
- Antenna theory.
- Direction-finding fundamentals.
- Principles on detecting and identifying frequencies of interest
- Compilation of EW running estimates.
- Joint spectrum interference report and EMI reporting procedures.
- Digital signal processing.
- Electromagnetic Warfare Planning and Management Tool familiarity and scenario planning.
- Fundamentals of maneuver.

G-7. Training and instructions from MTTs allow cyberspace operations and EW Soldiers to meet with military and commercial experts. MTTs provide added real-world insight and practices and to establish and maintain professional networks for increased operational efficiency at home station. Training lanes provide cyberspace operations and EW Soldiers the opportunity to exercise combining efforts that culminate home-station training and assist with ensuring unit readiness and survivability. Training lanes can include such simulations as communication jamming to provide realism that emphasizes the importance of primary, alternate, contingency, and emergency plans. Subordinate units can use information from training events by conducting after-action reviews to develop primary, alternate, contingency, and emergency plans.

COMBAT TRAINING CENTERS

G-8. The Army currently has three maneuver combat training centers: The National Training Center, at Fort Irwin, California; the Joint Readiness Training Center, at Fort Polk, Louisiana; and the Joint Multinational Readiness Center, in Hohenfels, Germany, and the Mission Command Training Program (MCTP) worldwide deployable combat training center. Combat training center training simulates real-world events by creating real-world scenarios that units may encounter during deployment. Operational forces assigned to combat training center s impose these real-world scenarios on units. Combat training centers evaluate rotational training units for combat readiness determined by the proactive and reactive measures taken to prevent or mitigate obstacles presented during real-world scenarios.

G-9. In a decisive action scenario, cyberspace operations and EW are essential to gaining and maintaining tactical advantages needed for a favorable resolution. Combat training centers continuously observe the rotational training units' ability to operate in an OE that includes simulated conflict and competition. Combat training centers assist commanders in assessing their units' overall combat readiness; proficiency in mission-essential task list related tasks, and those critical and essential tasks that require additional training. Commanders can then oversee the implementation of necessary changes to home-station training to improve proficiency.

Other books we publish on Amazon.com

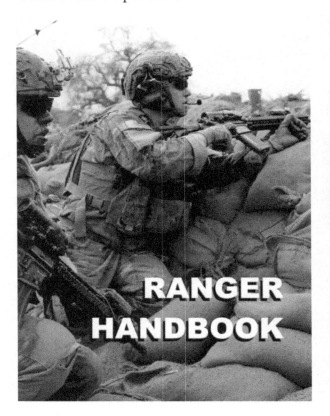

RANGER
HANDBOOK

TC 21-24
RAPPELLING

ATP 1-02.1

BREVITY

MULTI-SERVICE TACTICS,
TECHNIQUES, AND PROCEDURES
FOR MULTI-SERVICE BREVITY CODES

MAY 2021

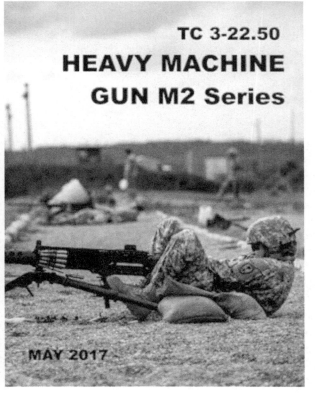

TC 3-22.50
HEAVY MACHINE
GUN M2 Series

MAY 2017

Glossary

This glossary lists acronyms and terms with Army, multi-Service, or joint definitions, and other selected terms. The proponent publication for a term is listed in parentheses after the definition.

SECTION I – ACRONYMS AND ABBREVIATIONS

AOR	area of responsibility
ARCYBER	United States Army Cyber Command
CCMD	combatant command
CEMA	cyberspace electromagnetic activities
CERF	cyber effects request format
CEWO	cyber electromagnetic warfare officer
CNMF	cyber national mission force
CNMF-HQ	Cyber National Mission Force-Headquarters
COA	course of action
CPT	cyber protection team
D3A	decide, detect, deliver, and assess
DCO	defensive cyberspace operations
DCO-IDM	defensive cyberspace operations-internal defensive measures
DCO-RA	defensive cyberspace operations-response actions
DODIN	Department of Defense information network
DODIN-A	Department of Defense information network-Army
EA	electromagnetic attack
EMI	electromagnetic interference
EMOE	electromagnetic operational environment
EMS	electromagnetic spectrum
EMSO	electromagnetic spectrum operations
EP	electromagnetic protection
ES	electromagnetic support
EW	electromagnetic warfare
I2CEWS	intelligence, information, cyber, electromagnetic warfare and space
IO	information operations
IP	Internet Protocol
IPB	intelligence preparation of the battlefield
JEMSO	joint electromagnetic spectrum operations
JEMSOC	joint electromagnetic spectrum operations cell
JFHQ-C	Joint Force Headquarters-Cyber

JFHQ-DODIN	Joint Force Headquarters-Department of Defense Information Network
JTF	joint task force
NCO	noncommissioned officer
NETCOM	United States Army Network Enterprise Technology Command
OCO	offensive cyberspace operations
OE	operational environment
OPLAN	operation plan
OPORD	operation order
OPSEC	operations security
RFS	request for support
SIGINT	signals intelligence
TSS	targeting sensing software
USC	United States Code
USCYBERCOM	United States Cyber Command

SECTION II – TERMS

adversary

A party acknowledged as potentially hostile to a friendly party and against which the use of force may be envisaged. (JP 3-0)

Army design methodology

A methodology for applying critical and creative thinking to understand, visualize, and describe problems and approaches to solving them. Also called **ADM**. (ADP 5-0)

assessment

1) A continuous process that measures the overall effectiveness of employing capabilities during military operations. **2) Determination of the progress toward accomplishing a task, creating a condition, or achieving an objective.** 3) Analysis of the security, effectiveness, and potential of an existing or planned intelligence activity. 4) Judgment of the motives, qualifications, and characteristics of present or prospective employees or "agents." (JP 3-0)

chaff

Radar confusion reflectors, consisting of thin, narrow metallic strips of various lengths and frequency responses, which are used to reflect echoes for confusion purposes. (JP 3-85)

combat power

The total means of destructive, constructive, and information capabilities that a military unit or formation can apply at a given time. (ADP 3-0)

constraint

A restriction placed on the command by a higher command. (FM 6-0)

countermeasures

That form of military science that, by the employment of devices and/or techniques, has as its objective the impairment of the operational effectiveness of enemy activity. (JP 3-85)

cyberspace

A global domain within the information environment consisting of the interdependent networks of information technology infrastructures and resident data, including the Internet, telecommunications networks, computer systems, and embedded processors and controllers. (JP 3-12)

cyberspace attack

Actions taken in cyberspace that create noticeable denial effects (i.e., degradation, disruption, or destruction) in cyberspace or manipulation that leads to denial that appears in a physical domain, and is considered a form of fires. (JP 3-12)

cyberspace electromagnetic activities

The process of planning, integrating, and synchronizing cyberspace operations and electromagnetic warfare operations in support of unified land operations. Also called **CEMA**. (ADP 3-0)

cyberspace exploitation

Actions taken in cyberspace to gain intelligence, maneuver, collect information, or perform other enabling actions required to prepare for future military operations. (JP 3-12)

cyberspace defense

Actions taken within protected cyberspace to defeat specific threats that have breached or are threatening to breach cyberspace security measures and include actions to detect, characterize, counter, and mitigate threats, including malware or the unauthorized activities of users, and to restore the system to a secure configuration. (JP 3-12)

cyberspace operations

The employment of cyberspace capabilities where the primary purpose is to achieve objectives in or through cyberspace. Also see **CO**. (JP 3-0)

cyberspace security

Actions taken within protected cyberspace to prevent unauthorized access to, exploitation of, or damage to computers, electronic communications systems, and other information technology, including platform information technology, as well as the information contained therein, to ensure its availability, integrity, authentication, confidentiality, and nonrepudiation. (JP 3-12)

defeat

To render a force incapable of achieving its objectives. (ADP 3-0)

defensive cyberspace operations

Missions to preserve the ability to utilize blue cyberspace capabilities and protect data, networks, cyberspace-enabled devices, and other designated systems by defeating on-going or imminent malicious cyberspace activity. Also called **DCO**. (JP 3-12)

defensive cyberspace operations-internal defensive measures

Operations in which authorized defense actions occur within the defended portion of cyberspace. Also called **DCO-IDM**. (JP 3-12)

defensive cyberspace operations-response actions

Operations that are part of a defensive cyberspace operations mission that are taken external to the defended network or portion of cyberspace without permission of the owner of the affected system. Also called **DCO-RA**. (JP 3-12)

Department of Defense information network

The set of information capabilities and associated processes for collecting, processing, storing, disseminating, and managing information on demand to warfighters, policy makers, and support personnel, whether interconnected or stand-alone. Also called **DODIN**. (JP 6-0)

Department of Defense information network-Army

An Army-operated enclave of the Department of Defense information network that encompasses all Army information capabilities that collect, process, store, display, disseminate, and protect information worldwide. Also called **DODIN-A**. (ATP 6-02.71)

Department of Defense information network operations

Operations to secure, configure, operate, extend, maintain, and sustain Department of Defense cyberspace to create and preserve the confidentiality, availability, and integrity of the Department of Defense information network. Also called **DODIN operations**. (JP 3-12)

directed energy

An umbrella term covering technologies that relate to the production of a beam of concentrated electromagnetic energy or atomic or subatomic particles. Also called **DE**. (JP 3-85)

directed-energy warfare

Military actions involving the use of directed-energy weapons, devices, and countermeasures. Also called **DEW**. (JP 3-85)

directed-energy weapon

A weapon or system that uses directed energy to incapacitate, damage, or destroy enemy equipment, facilities, and/or personnel. (JP 3-85)

direction finding

A procedure for obtaining bearings of radio frequency emitters by using a highly directional antenna and a display unit on an intercept receiver or ancillary equipment. Also called **DF**. (JP 3-85)

dynamic targeting

Targeting that prosecutes targets identified too late or not selected for action in time to be included in deliberate targeting. (JP 3-60)

electromagnetic attack

Division of electromagnetic warfare involving the use of electromagnetic energy, directed energy, or antiradiation weapons to attack personnel, facilities, or equipment with the intent of degrading, neutralizing, or destroying enemy combat capability and is considered a form of fires. Also called **EA**. (JP 3-85)

electromagnetic compatibility

The ability of systems, equipment, and devices that use the electromagnetic spectrum to operate in their intended environments without causing or suffering unacceptable or unintentional degradation because of electromagnetic radiation or response. Also called **EMC**. (JP 3-85)

electromagnetic hardening

Actions taken to protect personnel, facilities, and/or equipment by blanking, filtering, attenuating, grounding, bonding, and/or shielding against undesirable effects of electromagnetic energy. (JP 3-85)

electromagnetic masking

The controlled radiation of electromagnetic energy on friendly frequencies in a manner to protect the emissions of friendly communications and electronic systems against enemy electromagnetic support measures/signals intelligence without significantly degrading the operation of friendly systems. (JP 3-85)

electromagnetic intrusion

The intentional insertion of electromagnetic energy into transmission paths in any manner. The objective of electromagnetic intrusion is to deceive threat operators or cause confusion. (JP 3-85)

electromagnetic jamming

The deliberate radiation, reradiation, or reflection of electromagnetic energy for the purpose of preventing or reducing an enemy's effective use of the electromagnetic spectrum, and with the intent of degrading or neutralizing the enemy's combat capability. (JP 3-85)

electromagnetic probing

The intentional radiation designed to be introduced into the devices or systems of adversaries to learn the functions and operational capabilities of the devices or systems. (JP 3-85)

electromagnetic protection

Division of electromagnetic warfare involving actions taken to protect personnel, facilities, and equipment from any effects of friendly or enemy use of the electromagnetic spectrum that degrade, neutralize, or destroy friendly combat capability. Also called **EP**. (JP 3-85)

electromagnetic pulse

A strong burst of electromagnetic radiation caused by a nuclear explosion, energy weapon, or by natural phenomenon, that may couple with electrical or electronic systems to produce damaging current and voltage surges. (JP 3-85)

electromagnetic reconnaissance

The detection, location, identification, and evaluation of foreign electromagnetic radiations. (JP 3-85)

electromagnetic security

The protection resulting from all measures designed to deny unauthorized persons information of value that might be derived from their interception and study of noncommunications electromagnetic radiations (e.g., radar). (JP 3-85)

electromagnetic spectrum superiority

That degree of control in the electromagnetic spectrum that permits the conduct of operations at a given time and place without prohibitive interference, while affecting the threat's ability to do the same. (JP 3-85)

electromagnetic support

Division of electromagnetic warfare involving actions tasked by, or under the direct control of, an operational commander to search for, intercept, identify, and locate or localize sources of intentional and unintentional radiated electromagnetic energy for immediate threat recognition, targeting, planning, and conduct of future operations. Also called **ES**. (JP 3-85)

electromagnetic vulnerability

The characteristics of a system that cause it to suffer a definite degradation (incapability to perform the designated mission) as a result of having been subjected to a certain level of electromagnetic environmental effects. (JP 3-85)

electromagnetic warfare

Military action involving the use of electromagnetic and directed energy to control the electromagnetic spectrum or to attack the enemy. Also called **EW**. (JP 3-85)

electromagnetic warfare reprogramming

The deliberate alteration or modification of electromagnetic warfare or target sensing systems, or the tactics and procedures that employ them, in response to validated changes in equipment, tactics, or the electromagnetic environment. (JP 3-85)

enemy

An enemy is a party identified as hostile against which the use of force is authorized. (ADP 3-0)

essential task

A specified or implied task that must be executed to accomplish the mission. (FM 6-0)

execution

The act of putting a plan into action by applying combat power to accomplish the mission and adjusting operations based on changes in the situation. (ADP 5-0)

hazard

A condition with the potential to cause injury, illness, or death of personnel, damage to or loss of equipment or property, or mission degradation. (JP 3-33)

high-payoff target

A target whose loss to the enemy will significantly contribute to the success of the friendly course of action. Also called **HPT**. (JP 3-60)

high-value target

A target the enemy commander requires for the successful completion of the mission. (JP 3-60)

hybrid threat

A hybrid threat is the diverse and dynamic combination of regular forces, irregular forces, terrorists, or criminal elements acting in concert to achieve mutually benefitting effects. (ADP 3-0)

implied task

A task that must be performed to accomplish a specified task or mission but is not stated in the higher headquarters' order. (FM 6-0)

information collection

An activity that synchronizes and integrates the planning and employment of sensors and assets as well as the processing, exploitation, and dissemination systems in direct support of current and future operations. (FM 3-55)

information operations

The integrated employment, during military operations, of information-related capabilities in concert with other lines of operation to influence, disrupt, corrupt, or usurp the decision-making of adversaries and potential adversaries while protecting our own. Also called **IO**. (JP 3-13)

intelligence

1) The product resulting from the collection, processing, integration, evaluation, analysis, and interpretation of available information concerning foreign nations, hostile or potentially hostile forces or elements, or areas of actual or potential operations. 2) The activities that result in the product. 3) The organizations engaged in such activities. (JP 2-0)

intelligence operations

The tasks undertaken by military intelligence units through the intelligences disciplines to obtain information to satisfy validated requirements. (ADP 2-0)

intelligence preparation of the battlefield

The systematic process of analyzing the mission variables of enemy, terrain, weather, and civil considerations in an area of interest to determine their effect on operations. Also called **IPB**. (ATP 2-01.3)

knowledge management

The process of enabling knowledge flow to enhance shared understanding, learning, and decision making. (ADP 6-0)

named area of interest

The geospatial area or systems node or link against which information that will satisfy a specific information requirement can be collected. Also called **NAI**. (JP 2-01.3)

offensive cyberspace operations

Missions intended to project power in and through cyberspace. Also called **OCO**. (JP 3-12)

operational environment

A composite of the conditions, circumstances, and influences that affect the employment of capabilities and impact the decisions of the commander assigned responsibility for it. Also called **OE**. (JP 3-0)

operational initiative

The setting or tempo and terms of action throughout an operation. (ADP 3-0)

operations process

The major command and control activities performed during operations: planning, preparing, executing, and continuously assessing the operation. (ADP 5-0)

operations security

A capability that identifies and controls critical information, indicators of friendly force actions attendant to military operations, and incorporates countermeasures to reduce the risk of an adversary exploiting vulnerabilities. Also called **OPSEC**. (JP 3-13.3)

planning

The art and science of understanding a situation, envisioning a desired future, and laying out effective ways of bringing that future about. (ADP 5-0)

position of relative advantage

A location or the establishment of a favorable condition within the area of operations that provides the commander with temporary freedom of action to enhance combat power over an enemy or influence the enemy to accept risk and move to a position of disadvantage. (ADP 3.0)

preparation

Those activities performed by units and Soldiers to improve their ability to execute an operation. (ADP 5.0)

priority of fires

The commander's guidance to the staff, subordinate commanders, fires planners, and supporting agencies to employ fires in accordance with the relative importance of a unit's mission. (FM 3-09)

priority of support

A priority set by the commander to ensure a subordinate unit has support in accordance with its relative importance to accomplish the mission. (ADP 5-0)

radio frequency countermeasures

Any device or technique employing radio frequency materials or technology that is intended to impair the effectiveness of enemy activity, particularly with respect to precision-guided and sensor systems. (JP 3-85)

risk management

The process to identify, assess, and control risks and make decisions that balance risk cost with mission benefits. (JP 3-0)

scheme of fires

The detailed, logical sequence of targets and fire support events to find and engage targets to support commander's objectives. (JP 3-09)

specified task

A task specifically assigned to an organization by its higher headquarters. (FM 6-0)

sustainment warfighting function

The related tasks and systems that provide support and services to ensure freedom of action, extended operational reach, and prolong endurance. (ADP 3-0)

target

An entity or object that performs a function for the adversary considered for possible engagement or other actions. See also **objective area**. (JP 3-60)

target area of interest

The geographical area where high-valued targets can be acquired and engaged by friendly forces. (JP 2-01.3)

targeting

The process of selecting and prioritizing targets and matching the appropriate response to them, considering operational requirements and capabilities. (JP 3-0)

warfighting function

A group of tasks and systems united by a common purpose that commanders use to accomplish missions and training objectives. (ADP 3-0)

wartime reserve modes

Characteristics and operating procedures of sensor, communications, navigation aids, threat recognition, weapons, and countermeasure systems that will contribute to military effectiveness if unknown to or misunderstood by opposing commanders before they are used, but could be exploited or neutralized if known in advance. (JP 3-85)

References

All URLs accessed 24 May 2021.

REQUIRED PUBLICATIONS

These documents must be available to the intended users of this publication.

DOD Dictionary of Military and Associated Terms. January 2021.

FM 1-02.1. *Operational Terms.* 9 March 2021.

FM 1-02.2. *Military Symbols.* 10 November 2020.

RELATED PUBLICATIONS

DEPARTMENT OF DEFENSE PUBLICATIONS

Most DOD publications are available at the Executive Services Directorate Website at:
https://www.esd.whs.mil/DD/DoD-Issuances/.

DODI O-3115.07. *Signals Intelligence (SIGINT).* 15 September 2008 w/Change 2 dated 25 August 2020.

DODM 5240.01. Procedures Governing the Conduct of DOD Intelligence Activities. 8 August 2016.

JOINT PUBLICATIONS

Most Chairman of the Joint Chiefs of Staff Publications are available at:
https://www.jcs.mil/Library/CJCS-Instructions/

Most Joint Publications are available online: https://www.jcs.mil/Doctrine/Joint-Doctine-Pubs/.

CJCSI 3211.01F. *Joint Policy for Military Deception.* 14 May 2015.

CJCSI 3370.01C. *Target Development Standards.* 14 August 2018. Limited (.mil/.gov only)

JP 2-0. *Joint Intelligence.* 22 October 2013.

JP 2-01. *Joint and National Intelligence Support to Military Operations.* 5 July 2017.

JP 2-01.3. *Joint Intelligence Preparation of the Operational Environment.* 21 May 2014.

JP 3-0. *Joint Operations.* 17 January 2017.

JP 3-09. *Joint Fire Support.* 10 April 2019.

JP 3-12. *Cyberspace Operations.* 8 June 2018.

JP 3-13. *Information Operations.* 27 November 2012 w/Change 1 dated 20 November 2014.

JP 3-13.3. *Operations Security.* 6 January 2016.

JP 3-14. *Space Operations.* 10 April 2018 w/Change 1 dated 26 October 2020

JP 3-33. *Joint Task Force Headquarters.* 31 January 2018.

JP 3-60. *Joint Targeting.* 28 September 2018.

JP 3-85. *Joint Electromagnetic Spectrum Operations.* 22 May 2020.

JP 5-0. *Joint Planning.* 1 December 2020.

JP 6-0. *Joint Communications System.* 10 June 2015 w/Change 1 dated 4 October 2019.

ARMY PUBLICATIONS

Unless otherwise indicated, Army publications are available online: https://armypubs.army.mil.

ADP 1. *The Army*. 31 July 2019.

ADP 2-0. *Intelligence*. 31 July 2019.

ADP 3-0. *Operations*. 31 July 2019.

ADP 3-19. *Fires*. 31 July 2019.

ADP 3-37. *Protection*. 31 July 2019.

ADP 3-90. *Offense and Defense*. 31 July 2019.

ADP 5-0. *The Operations Process*. 31 July 2019.

ADP 6-0. *Mission Command: Command and Control of Army Forces*. 31 July 2019.

AR 195-2. *Criminal Investigation Activities*. 21 July 2020.

AR 380-10. *Foreign Disclosure and Contacts with Foreign Representatives*. 14 July 2015.

AR 380-5. *Army Information Security Program*. 22 October 2019.

AR 381-10. *U.S. Army Intelligence Activities*. 3 May 2007.

AR 381-12. *Threat Awareness and Reporting Program*. 1 June 2016.

AR 525-21. (U) *Army Military Deception (MILDEC) Program (C)*. 28 October 2013

AR 530-1. *Operations Security*. 26 September 2014.

ATP 2-01.3. *Intelligence Preparation of the Battlefield*. 1 March 2019.

ATP 3-09.32. *Multi-Service Tactics, Techniques, and Procedures for Joint Application of Firepower (JFIRE)*. 18 October 2019.

ATP 3-12.3. *Electronic Warfare Techniques*. 16 July 2019.

ATP 3-13.3. *Operations Security for Division and Below*. 16 June 2019.

ATP 3-60. *Targeting*. 7 May 2015.

ATP 3-60.1/MCRP 3-31.5/NTTP 3-60.1/AFTTP 3-2.3. *Multi-Service Tactics, Techniques, and Procedures for Dynamic Targeting*. 10 September 2015.

ATP 3-94.2. *Deep Operations*. 1 September 2016.

ATP 5-19. *Risk Management*. 14 April 2014.

ATP 6-01.1. *Techniques for Effective Knowledge Management*. 6 March 2015.

ATP 6-02.70. *Techniques for Spectrum Management Operations*. 16 October 2019.

ATP 6-02.71. *Techniques for Department of Defense Information Network Operations*. 30 April 2019.

FM 2-0. *Intelligence*. 6 July 2018.

FM 3-0. *Operations*. 6 October 2017.

FM 3-09. *Fire Support and Field Artillery Operations*. 30 April 2020

FM 3-13. *Information Operations*. 6 December 2016.

FM 3-13.4. *Army Support to Military Deception*. 26 February 2019.

FM 3-14. *Army Space Operations*. 30 October 2019.

FM 3-55. *Information Collection*. 3 May 2013.

FM 6-0. *Commander and Staff Organization and Operations*. 5 May 2014.

FM 6-02. *Signal Support to Operations*. 13 September 2019.

FM 6-27. MCTP 11-10C. *The Commander's Handbook on the Law of Land Warfare*. 7 August 2019.

OTHER PUBLICATIONS

Most Code of Federal Regulations are available at https://www.ecfr.gov/.

Department of Defense Electromagnetic Spectrum Superiority Strategy. October 2020. https://www.defense.gov/Newsroom/Publications/

European-U.S. Privacy Shield. 12 July 2016. https://www.privacyshield.gov/

Executive Order 12333. United States Intelligence Activities. 4 December 1981. Amended by
Executive Order 13284 (2003) and 13470 (2008).
http://www.archives.gov/federal-register/codification/executive-order/12333.html

House of Representatives Bill 4081 - Consumer Privacy Protection Act of 2017.
https://www.congress.gov/bill/115th-congress/house-bill/4081

Title 17, Code of Federal Regulations. Commodity and Securities Exchanges.

Title 21, Code of Federal Regulations. Food and Drug.

Title 45, Code of Federal Regulations. Public Welfare.

Title 48, Code of Federal Regulations. Defense Federal Acquisition Regulation.

United States Constitution. https://www.whitehouse.gov/1600/constitution

UNITED STATES LAW

Most acts and public laws are available at https://uscode.house.gov/ .

Title 6, United States Code. Domestic Security.

Title 10, United States Code. Armed Forces.

Title 10, United States Code. Chapter 47, Uniform Code of Military Justice.

Title 15, United States Code. Commerce and Trade.

Title 18, United States Code. Crimes and Criminal Procedure.

Title 28, United States Code. Judiciary and Judicial Procedure.

Title 32, United States Code. National Guard.

Title 40, United States Code. Public Buildings, Property, and Works.

Title 44, United States Code. Public Printing and Documents.

Title 50, United States Code. War and National Defense.

PRESCRIBED FORMS

This section contains no entries.

REFERENCED FORMS

Unless otherwise indicated, DA forms are available on the Army Publishing Directorate website at
https://armypubs.army.mil/. DD forms are available on the Executive Services Directorate
website at https://www.esd.whs.mil/Directives/forms/.

DA Form 2028. *Recommended Changes to Publications and Blank Forms.*

Department of Defense forms are available on the Washington Headquarters Website:
https://www.esd.whs.mil/Directives/forms/

DD Form 1494. *Application for Equipment Frequency Allocation.*

DD Form 1972. *Joint Tactical Air Strike Request.*

Other books we publish on Amazon.com

Customer reviews

★★★★⯪ 4.6 out of 5

Customer reviews

★★★☆☆ 3 out of 5

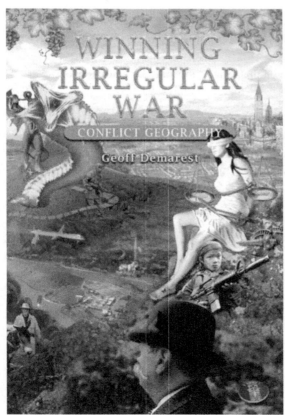

Index

Entries are by paragraph number.

1

1st Information Operations Command, 3-11

A

ARCYBER. *See* U.S. Army Cyber Command

Army design methodology, A-3

Army Information Warfare Operations Center, 3-5

C

CEMA. *See* cyberspace electromagnetic activities

CERF. *See* cyberspace effects request format

combatant commands, D-36

competition continuum, 1-44

Congested Environment, 1-31

contested Environment, 1-32

Core Competencies, 1-6

cyber combat mission force, D-25

cyber electromagnetic warfare officer, 3-24

cyber mission force, D-24

cyber national mission force, D-28, D-31

cyber protection brigade, 3-9

cyber protection force, D-27

cyber warfare officer, 3-25

cyberspace
risks, 4-88

cyberspace, 1-20

cyberspace actions
cyberspace attack, 2-20
cyberspace exploitation, 2-19
cyberspace security, 2-17

cyberspace actions, 2-16

cyberspace effects request format, E-16

cyberspace electromagnetic activities, 3-20
working group, 3-32

network layers
cyber-persona , 1-26
logical , 1-25
physical , 1-23

cyberspace operations, 2-3
defensive
internal defensive measures, 2-10
response actions, 2-12
defensive, 2-12
taxonomy, 2-3

D

Defense Information Systems Agency, D-10

Defense Intelligence Agency, D-13

Department of Defense Information Network Operations, 2-5

DIA. *See* Defense Intelligence Agency

directed energy, 2-28

DISA. *See* Defense Information Systems Agency

E

EARF. *See* electromagnetic attack request format

electromagnetic attack
countermeasures, 2-30
deception, 2-31
meaconing, 2-35

electromagnetic attack
tasks, 2-26

electromagnetic attack
intrusion, 2-32

electromagnetic attack
jamming, 2-33

electromagnetic attack
probing, 2-34

electromagnetic attack request format, E-30

electromagnetic compatibility, 2-42

electromagnetic hardening, 2-43

electromagnetic masking, 2-46

electromagnetic protection
deconfliction, 2-40
tasks, 2-38

electromagnetic pulse, 2-29

electromagnetic security, 2-48

electromagnetic spectrum, 1-28

electromagnetic support
reconnaissance, 2-55

electromagnetic support
tasks, 2-53

electromagnetic support, 1-62

electromagnetic support
threat warning, 2-57

electromagnetic support
direction finding, 2-59

electromagnetic support, 2-60

electromagnetic warfare
airborne, E-27
countermeasures, 2-47
attack, 2-22
protection, 2-36
support, 2-50
organizations, 3-13
platoon, 3-14
reprogramming, F-1
reprogramming, 2-61
taxonomy, 2-21

Electromagnetic warfare, 2-21

electromagnetic warfare NCO, 3-30

electromagnetic warfare
NCOIC, 3-27—3-29

electromagnetic warfare
sergeant major, 3-27—3-29

electromagnetic warfare
technician, 3-26

emission control, 2-44

Entries are by paragraph number.

F

fires support element, 3-39
fundamental principles, 1-3

H

hazards, 1-40

I

I2CEWS, 3-18
information collection, 4-40
information operations officer, 3-37
integration, 4-19
   host nation, C-13
   installation, C-14
   interagency and intergovernmental, C-4
   joint, C-1
   multinational, C-8
   nongovernmental, C-12
   private industry, C-15
intelligence, 4-47
intelligence preparation of the battlefield, 1-58, 4-21
intelligence staff, 3-35

   information operations, 2-76
   intelligence, 2-64
   space operations, 2-69
IPB. *See* intelligence preparation of the battlefield

J

JCC. *See* joint cyber center
JFHQ-Cyber. *See* Joint Force Headquarters Cyberspace
JFHQ-DODIN. *See* Joint Force Headquarters DODIN
joint cyber center, D-38
Joint Force Headquarters-DODIN, D-34

K

key terrain, 4-53
knowledge management, 4-102

M

MDMP. *See* military decision-making process
military decision-making process, A-6

step 1 – receipt of mission, A-8
step 2 – mission analysis, A-11
step 3 – course of action development, A-25
step 4 – course of action analysis and war-gaming, A-40
step 5 – course of action comparison, A-46
step 6 – course of action approval, A-50
step 7 – orders production, dissemination, and transition, A-53
multi-domain battlefield, 1-46

N

National Geospatial Intelligence Agency, D-15
National Guard Bureau, D-19
National Reconnaissance Office, D-17
National Security Agency, D-8
NETCOM. *See* U.S. Army Network Enterprise Technology Command
NGIA. *See* National Geospatial Intelligence Agency
NRO. *See* National Reconnaissance Office
NSA. *See* National Security Agency

O

cyberspace operatons offensive, 2-14
operation order
   annex C, A-56—A-57
   appendix 12, A-58
Operational Environment, 1-1
   trends, 1-29
Operational Environment, 1-1
operations process
   assessment, 4-17
   execution, 4-12
   planning, 4-4
operations process, 4-2
OPORD. *See* operation order
organizations
   Department of Defense, D-6
   national, D-1

P

planning
   methodologies, A-1
operations process, 4-10, 4-12

R

reconnaissance, 4-48
request for effects, E-15
request for support
   Defensive cyberspace, E-8
   offensive cyberspace, E-5
risk management, 4-85
rules of engagement, B-3

S

Service cyberspace components, D-33
signal staff, 3-36
signals intelligence, 2-60
signals intelligence, 1-62
spectrum manager, 3-38
spectrum manager, 3-31
staff judge advocate, 3-40
surveillance, 4-49

T

targeting, 4-58
   considerations, 4-76
   crosswalk, 4-13
   functions, 4-67
threat, 1-33
training, G-1
   combat training centers, G-8
   home-station, G-4
   institutional, G-3

U

U.S. Army Cyber Command, 3-3
U.S. Army Network Enterprise Technology Command, 3-7
U.S. Army Reserve, D-21

   Joint Force Headquarters-Cyberspace, D-34
U.S. Cyber Command, D-22
United States Code, B-8

Entries are by paragraph number.

USCYBERCOM. *See* U.S. Cyber Command

W

warfighting functions, 1-48
    command and control, 1-49

fires, 1-64
intelligence, 1-56
movement and maneuver, 1-51
protection, 1-68
sustainment, 1-66

wartime reserve modes, 2-49

By Order of the Secretary of the Army:

JAMES C. MCCONVILLE
General, United States Army
Chief of Staff

Official:

MARK F. AVERILL
Acting Administrative Assistant
to the Secretary of the Army
2120804

DISTRIBUTION:
Active Army, Army National Guard, and United States Army Reserve. Distributed in electronic media only(EMO).

Hand Signals

I Think I Saw Something

Did You Mean Me? (confirmation requested)

Looks Clear - No Need To Be Quiet

Speak Up

I'm Having A Hard Time Seeing Very Far Without My Glasses

Aim for The Ass

I Can't Reach This Pocket (assistance requested)

I Have Been Hit (showing approximate size of hole)

Something's Wrong With My Gun (repeat gesture to add "...again!" to indicate frustration)